Old Ardnamurchan, Moidart, Sunart, and Ardgour

Guthrie Hutton

Lochaline Pier and Pier House.

© Guthrie Hutton, 2012
First published in the United Kingdom, 2012,
by Stenlake Publishing Ltd.
01290 551122
www.stenlake.co.uk

ISBN 9781840336009

Acknowledgements

In the early 1960s my mother, my sister and myself headed for Loch Sunart. It was a wet day and cloud obscured everything until it lifted and the rain eased to reveal a glorious sunset and a stunning view. We stopped at a bed and breakfast at Strontian where our hostess dismissed the notion that it was unfair to have to pay tax for such dreadful roads (as they were then), because it gave her the right to drive her little car on busy roads in populous places. It was her idea of getting away from it all and a glorious contradiction of a tired cliché. Compiling this little book has revived the memory of that conversation which made me see things differently then and made me chuckle now, so I have a lot to thank her for. I was helped in more tangible ways by my companion on that journey, my sister, who put me up, or more accurately put up with me, while I conducted research for this book. I must also thank the Kithead Trust and the cheery staff at Fort William Library for helping me to unearth some elusive details.

Further Reading

The books listed below were used by the author during his research. None are available from Stenlake Publishing; please contact your local bookshop or reference library.

Atkinson, Tom, *Roads to the Isles,* 1983.
Duckworth, C. and Langmuir, G., *West Highland Steamers,* 1967.
Gaskell, Philip, *Morvern Transformed,* 1968.
Gifford, John, *The Buildings of Scotland: Highlands and Islands,* 1992.
Haldane, A. R. B., *New Ways Through the Glens,* 1962.
Maclean, Allan, *Telford's Highland Churches,* 1989.
Maclean, Loraine, *Discovering Inverness-shire,* 1988.
McGregor, John, *100 Years of the West Highland Railway,* 1994.
Miers, Mary, *The Western Seaboard,* 2008.
Weir, Marie, *Ferries in Scotland,* 1988.

David MacBrayne's little cargo steamer *Handa* is seen here in Loch Sunart off Strontian.

Introduction

The area containing Ardnamurchan, Moidart, Sunart, Morvern, and Ardgour is big, with long lochs and high mountains. It is almost an island, with three-quarters of it surrounded by water. In places it can look bleak and desolate, while other parts are stunningly beautiful and the epitome of scenic grandeur and beauty. The population that lives amongst this magnificence is small and scattered, with few villages of any size. Some major improvements have been made, but for a long time it was difficult to get around on barely adequate roads.

It was not always so. In the distant past, when water was seen as a highway, and not a barrier, the long coastline gave the area significant advantages. It was at the centre of trading routes along the west coast, through the Sound of Mull and on lochs that penetrated far inland. To protect these routes great coastal castles were built and powerful clans grew around them. They honed their warrior skills in feuding and fighting, as clans tended to do, but when the call came in 1745 those who had clung to the old religion marched to the beat of the rebel drum. They followed Bonnie Prince Charlie to the bitter end at Culloden and endured punitive reprisals in the aftermath.

Weakened, the clan system began to fall apart. Shorn of their estates the chiefs had no need of fighting men and the glens began to empty as emigration severed the bonds of kinship. The government started to build roads, which provided some employment, but with new owners buying up ancient clan lands the pace of emigration increased in the face of an invasion of sheep. Those dispossessed people who did not leave clung on in small communities, mainly on the coast. Profits from sheep farming dipped after a while and the estates were turned over to the sport of killing wildlife. Great houses and shooting lodges were built, in contrast to the little indigenous thatched dwellings.

Crofting legislation at the latter end of the nineteenth century began to redress the balance and steamers started to bring in people from a curious outside world. Lighthouses became features in the landscape. The railway too made inroads, arriving first at Fort William and then skirting the northern edge on the way to Mallaig. Mining for lead at Strontian and sand at Lochaline brought employment, but people continued to drift away. The emptiness of the area and ease of isolating it attracted the Second World War military authorities, in search of places to carry out secretive training of special forces. Since then the emphasis has been on opening up the area with new roads and modern ferries, and against the odds the railway has survived. It means that this land of stunning views and quiet corners is more accessible and easier to get around, but despite the intrusions of the modern world this remains a special place.

The Loch Shiel steamer, *Clanranald II*, at Acharacle Pier.

At the end of the long and winding (and hilly) road along the Ardnamurchan Peninsula is the lighthouse that sits at the British mainland's most westerly point. Designed by Alan Stevenson of the famous lighthouse-building Stevenson family, it was built using the distinctive pink granite from the Ross of Mull, a stone much favoured by engineers for its strength. It was also admired for its appearance and the Ardnamurchan Lighthouse was never painted, but left as a 100 foot high tower of shining natural stone. Completed in 1848, the light remained as a manned station until it was automated in 1986. It has since been turned into a visitor centre.

Ardnamurchan Point

Photographer, writer, eccentric and authority on all things Highland, Mary Ethel Muir Donaldson built the house known as Sanna Bheag in 1927. Situated to the north of the lighthouse, the house is seen here looking towards the Small Isles in the distance. In an attempt to marry the Arts and Crafts movement with the traditions of croft houses, like those at nearby Achnaha, Miss Donaldson used local people and masons from Tobermory, and helped with some of the work herself. A keen carpenter she put her woodworking skills to good use by making the gates in the perimeter wall. Destroyed by fire in 1947 the house was made habitable again twenty years later, but without many of the original features.

Ardnamurchan, Sanna

Travelling to and from Kilchoan was not easy. On the left, a Morris saloon car has been stopped in a passing place while its occupants savour the view of the Small Isles, and take a break from the road: they described this as 'the only good bit'. The photograph is one of a number in this book taken from an album that recorded a holiday in 1948 enjoyed by a group of ladies from Fife. Although they came from a flat part of the country, they evidently thrived among the western hills.

The journey by sea could also be tricky. The outer islands mail boat operating out of Oban stopped in the 1930s and 40s on her way through the Sound of Mull and stood off Kilchoan, where she was met by this little boat named *Kilchoan*. Passengers destined for, or boarding from, the village had to scramble between the little flit boat and the larger ship, in this case thought to be the steamer *Lochearn*. Goods were also transferred, although with a little less ceremony than the people.

Steamer operators David MacBrayne Ltd. were awarded a new mail contract in 1947 which specified an improved service to Ardnamurchan, specifically a ferry between Tobermory and Mingarry. The first boat to operate this run was the *Lochbuie*, a former RAF rescue boat that was refitted at Dumbarton and re-launched in March 1949. As soon as she started work on the six mile crossing the practice of stopping the outer islands mail boat off Kilchoan was discontinued. *Lochbuie* is seen here in the early 1950s approaching Mingarry Pier. This passenger-only boat has since been replaced by a modern car ferry. It has improved Kilchoan's links with the wider world by giving access through Mull to Craignure and the Oban ferry.

Ardnamurchan, Mingarry

Sitting on a natural rocky eminence, and with enclosure walls almost fifty feet high, Mingarry Castle is an imposing structure commanding the Sound of Mull and the entrance to Loch Sunart. Dating from the thirteenth century it later became the stronghold of the MacIans of Ardnamurchan, a sept of the Lords of the Isles, the Macdonalds of Islay. This connection made it the ideal place for King James IV to come twice in the late fifteenth century to receive submissions from the Clan Chiefs. Despite having their power suppressed the clans continued to wage war on one another and the castle changed hands a number of times until the Campbells eventually got control of Ardnamurchan.

Ardnamurchan, Mingarry

The Campbells cashed in early in the nineteenth century, after which the Ardnamurchan estates changed hands a number of times. During his time as owner Sir James Riddell began to clear tenants from the land to establish sheep runs and this process was continued under the next landlord James Dalgleish. He sold out to Charles D. Rudd, a colonial adventurer and friend of Cecil Rhodes who had made a fortune out of African diamond mines. In his time as owner he built Glenborrodale Castle, a massive pile of Dumfriesshire sandstone. The architect, Sydney Mitchell, was also responsible for other estate buildings that go largely to make up the estate village of Glenborrodale.

Ardnamurchan, Glenborrodale

Many, perhaps most, goods came in and out of the area by sea and one of the busiest jetties was at Salen on Loch Sunart, where the natural rock beside a little bay was adapted to provide a mooring for small vessels. On the right, in an early twentieth century picture, the puffer *Mallard* has come alongside and appears to be unloading coal. She is typical of the type of vessel made famous in the stories of *Para Handy* and the *Vital Spark*. They provided a lifeline to small communities on the west coast, but offered few creature comforts to the crew - the canvas dodger in front of the funnel was the only protection the helmsman had against the weather.

Ardnamurchan, Salen

The coaster *Lochshiel*, a somewhat better appointed vessel than the early puffers, is seen here on the left approaching Salen Jetty in the 1940s. Built at Leith for David MacBrayne Ltd., she was launched in August 1929 and operated on a route that took in Mull, the Firth of Lorne and Loch Leven, as well as Loch Sunart. She could carry up to 200 tons of often very varied cargo as the picture on the right shows, with a cart being unloaded by the ship's own derrick. The same shipment also appears to have included the horse, to pull the cart, and a cow for another owner. *Lochshiel* remained in service up to 1952.

Ardnamurchan, Salen

The ladies from Fife, whose car is seen on page 6, appear to have been based at Salen for their holiday. From here they ventured to other places, but spent a lot of their time walking and picnicking in the local area. Clustered around the head of an inlet off Loch Sunart, Salen is not large, nor is it the only place to bear the name, because there is another Salen on Mull. The two villages sit at the head of inlets called Salen Bay: the Gaelic name means a little sea, bay or inlet, so there is no mystery here for people who love to speculate about place-name origins. The holiday snapshots show the village looking west across the bay and a picnic beside Loch Sunart, with the distinctive Ben Resipol in the distance.

Ardnamurchan, Salen

After the stresses of the Second World War, Salen must have seemed like an oasis of peace and tranquillity, where people could recharge their spirits. Here, in the upper left picture, two of the Fife ladies are seen leaning on the parapet of 'Mr. McPherson's Bridge' over the Allt an t-Sailean, while sheep wander by unconcerned. Another of the ladies can be seen in the foreground of the upper right picture, sitting above the Strontian Road, reading. Below is the Salen Hotel, a small Victorian hostelry that has been somewhat modified over the years. The Acharacle road, which can be seen disappearing into the distance, has also been upgraded and realigned where it passes the hotel.

Sunart, Salen

Acharacle, at the southern end of Loch Shiel, is the principal settlement site in the area. It has been a stopping off point for visitors for many years, as can be seen from these pictures from the inter-war years. The upper picture shows the Ardshealach Private Hotel with a bell tent on the left that hints at a more basic level of self-catering accommodation than modern tourists might expect. Loch Shiel Hotel (lower) was built as a hunting lodge in the late nineteenth century, but had become a hotel by 1933 when this picture was taken. Stalking, by arrangement, was still being offered in the 1980s, but the interests of the customers have changed over the years to include, biking, boat trips and kayaking. Bus tours also stop off, giving the driver some respite from single-track roads.

Ardnamurchan, Acharacle

Acharacle was a place of contrasts, reflecting the wider area in microcosm. Large house, like Druimbeg (upper), sat in private grounds alongside the more traditional thatched buildings in the lower picture. The strips of cultivation running down towards Loch Shiel show the kind of crofting landscape once typical in the Highlands. The picture was taken in the late nineteenth century, about a decade after the passing of the Crofters Holdings (Scotland) Acts of 1886 and 1887 which gave tenants in seven 'crofting counties' security of tenure. The legislation was based on the findings of a Royal Commission set up in 1883 under Lord Napier to investigate the conditions that had been created after half a century of indiscriminate evictions.

Ardnamurchan, Acharacle

The pattern of cultivation strips is also evident in this early twentieth century picture of Arivegaig, a crofting community to the west of Acharacle. In the background is the Kentra Moss, a handy place for cutting peats for winter fuel. Standing dutifully on the road in the foreground is a horse harnessed to a cart. There appears to be no obvious handler with the animal, it is just standing there, which suggests that it may have been the photographer who left it while they climbed up to the higher ground to take the picture. In later years photographers became adept at leaving their cars in strategic places to add foreground interest to a wide view and this could be an early example of the practice.

Ardnamurchan, Arivegaig

To the west of Kentra Moss is Ardtoe where these thatched cottages and cultivation strips were photographed early in the twentieth century. Crofting had dwindled somewhat by 1975 when the Government's White Fish Authority moved its shellfish cultivation unit from North Wales to Ardtoe. Here, in this pristine marine environment, researchers could conduct experiments into the breeding and farming of sea fish like cod, halibut and other species. This beautiful coast, indented with sandy bays, has been popular with holidaymakers for decades. Postcard messages bear this out: 'it is warm here, I am very much sunburnt' said one in 1916 while another a few years later was 'enjoying the holidays although the weather isn't too good'. As ever in the west of Scotland, the weather is what you make it!

Ardnamurchan, Ardtoe

The grand mansion of Shielbridge House, on the left of this early twentieth century picture, was an earlier building that was extensively modified in 1898 by the architect Sydney Mitchell for the new owner Charles D. Rudd. The paint had barely dried when a fire in 1900 caused extensive damage, but Rudd, who also built Glenborrodale Castle, did not get rich by succumbing to little setbacks like that and the house was quickly rebuilt. It stood for another half century before it was demolished. On the right of the picture is the old Shiel Bridge designed by Thomas Telford and built in 1804 to carry the road from Corran to Kinlochmoidart. The three-arched bridge that superseded it, a little upstream, was erected in 1899.

Ardnamurchan/Moidart, Shielbridge

Dorlin House, a grand mansion built in the Scots Baronial style, may have incorporated an earlier laird's house. It was completed in 1864 for James Hope-Scott who had acquired Loch Shiel Estate a few years earlier. He sold the estate in 1871 to Lord Howard of Glossop who was followed by his son and other owners until 1940 when the Royal Navy moved in. The remote coastal location of the house, away from prying eyes, made it an ideal place to train service personnel in a variety of skills associated with amphibious landings and beach signals. Known from 1942 as HMS Dorlin it remained in use until the Allied invasions of Italy and France had been accomplished. After the war it lay empty and was blown up in 1964.

Moidart, Dorlin

If the builders of Castle Tioram chose the site for its natural beauty, they did well, although defence would have been a more likely consideration. Situated on a tidal island in Loch Moidart, the earliest part of the structure is a 12th century perimeter wall that, like the one at Mingarry, follows the shape of the rock on which it is built. The castle became part of the estate of Lady Amie, the estranged wife of John, Lord of the Isles, and was inherited by her son, Ranald MacDonald, founder of the powerful Clan Ranald. It remained their stronghold until 1715 when the then chief, Alan, had it (and other Clan Ranald houses) burned, fearing the outcome of that Jacobite Rebellion. Ruined, but still standing, it is seen here in pictures taken by the ladies from Fife in 1948. Their car is also seen stopped on the road between Acharacle and Dorlin.

Moidart, Dorlin/Castle Tioram

The island-studded split channel of the entrance to Loch Moidart is scenic splendour at its most breathtaking. At its core is Eilean Shona where this shooting lodge was built, probably at the turn of the eighteenth and nineteenth centuries. Typical of a type dotted around the Highlands it is situated at the eastern end of the island with a view of Castle Tioram. Originally Clanranald lands, the island was sold in the nineteenth century. A succession of owners then took it in turn to carry out improvements and in particular to clothe the eastern end of the island in a variety trees. Some of this planting is seen surrounding the house in this picture from around 1900.

Moidart, Eilean Shona

Dalilea House is situated on the northern shore of Loch Shiel, to the east of Acharacle. It is seen here in the 1950s when a young lady who was staying there wrote to her friend 'nice horses, great time, good weather, smashing food, sore bottom'! The house was modified early in the twentieth century with the addition of the top floor, turrets, crow steps and porch, which altered the appearance from the way it looked when it was built 100 years earlier. There was clearly an earlier house here because it is noted as the birthplace of the Gaelic poet Alasdair mac Mhaighster Alasdair who earned his living as a schoolmaster before joining the Jacobite Rebellion in 1745 as a captain in Clanranald's regiment. Dalilea was also the place where Bonnie Prince Charlie boarded the boat that took him to the head of Loch Shiel, to raise his standard and set in train the events that were to wreck so much of the Highland way of life.

Moidart, Dalilea

The contrast between some of the grand houses of the rich landowners and this little hut could scarcely be greater. The picture, taken in the early years of the twentieth century, was entitled 'Moidart, A Crofter's Hut'. As a wooden shack, the structure is untypical of traditional croft houses and rather than being a crofter's dwelling it may have been that of a cottar, a tenant whose house had no land attached to it. If crofters were poor, landless cottars were poorer and they had to find a way of living that didn't involve growing their own food. They generally suffered badly during the Clearances, but the Crofting Acts also gave them security of tenure, although not necessarily a way of earning a living.

Moidart

Bonnie Prince Charlie landed on the mainland near Arisaig in 1745, but before moving on to raise his standard at Glenfinnan he spent a few days at Kinlochmoidart House. Seven supporters who accompanied him each planted a beech tree and these became known as the seven men of Moidart. This must have been a heady time for the Jacobite Macdonalds, with the prince as a guest in their house and hope in the air. All that had gone the following year when Donald Macdonald had been captured and executed, his family evicted and the house burned. The estate was forfeited, then recovered in 1785, but in the late nineteenth century, with debts mounting, the Macdonalds sold out to a new proprietor. He commissioned a new Kinlochmoidart House, which was completed about 1885.

Moidart, Kinlochmoidart

William Leiper, the architect of the new Kinlochmoidart House, also designed or modified other estate buildings, including this old school and school house which was used for a time as the Kinlochmoidart Stores. It was not perhaps the level of industry envisaged in the early nineteenth century when the engineer Thomas Telford was given the task of building roads to improve infrastructure, communications and employment in the Highlands. One of the roads ran from an improved Corran Ferry to Kinlochmoidart. Its construction was fraught with difficulties, not least because the contractor proved unreliable and prone to seeking payment for work that he hadn't done. For years the road ended here, but that changed in the 1960s when a new road was made through Glenuig to Inverailort.

Moidart, Kinlochmoidart

On the 21st of January 1897 Lady Margaret Cameron of Lochiel cut the first sod to start construction on the extension to the West Highland Railway. Soon the sparsely populated route between Banavie and Mallaig was teeming with people and nowhere more than Lochailort where the contractor 'Concrete' Bob McAlpine set up his largest navvy camp with accommodation for 2,000 men. It also had an eight-bed hospital staffed by a doctor and two nurses, the first such facility on a British construction site. Ironically the most high profile patient was McAlpine's son, Malcolm, who was dreadfully injured in an explosion, but survived thanks to a remarkable rescue operation. Lochailort Station and the railway can be seen on the hillside, beyond the foreground buildings.

26

Moidart, Lochailort

Before the coming of the railway Inverailort must have been similar to the rest of Moidart with a scatter of humble dwellings contrasting with the grand houses of the well-to-do. The principal 'big' houses were Inverailort Castle and the smaller Glenshian House seen here. It formed part of the estate bought from the Macdonalds in 1828 by Major General Sir Alexander Cameron whose fifteen year old grand-daughter Christian inherited the estate in 1875. Sixty-five years later, with the country at war, Mrs Cameron-Head, as she then was, received notice that the military authorities intended to take over the houses for training special forces. She never recovered from the shock of returning to find soldiers clumsily and carelessly removing their contents. After the war Glenshian was used as a hotel before conversion into a sporting lodge.

Moidart, Lochailort

It took two days for the rowers to speed Bonnie Prince Charlie from Dalilea to the head of Loch Shiel where they arrived on 19th August 1745. Only a few men came with the prince and not many welcomed him, but gradually the numbers swelled as the Jacobite clans gathered in support. The standard was raised, speeches were spoken, scabbards were thrown away and the fateful Rebellion was under way. Seventy years later, a monument, designed by the architect James Gillespie Graham for Alexander Macdonald of Glenaladale, was erected to commemorate the event. His successor Angus Macdonald modified it some years later, and had a sculpted figure of a Highlander placed on top, as a more fitting tribute to the men who had fought and died in the ill-starred venture. It has been in the care of the National Trust for Scotland since 1938.

Moidart, Glenfinnan

Protected by their remote surroundings many clans resisted Protestantism and remained Episcopalian or Roman Catholic. Their religious loyalties made them staunch supporters of the Stuart cause and although this brought suffering, people remained true to their faith. Catholics also endured restrictions on where they could hold services, but these were lifted by the Emancipation Act of 1829, allowing places of worship like the Church of Our Lady and St. Finnan to be built at Glenfinnan in 1873. Designed by the architect Edward Welby Pugin it was paid for by Macdonald of Glenaladale, but he appears to have run out of money because, instead of being mounted in a tower, the bell was placed outside on the stone cradle seen in the picture on the right.

Moidart, Glenfinnan

Harry Potter's Hogwarts Express, steaming over 'Concrete' Bob MacAlpine's amazing curved viaduct, has made Glenfinnan familiar to people all over the world, but long before the railway came through a new road had made the area accessible to the outside world. Begun in 1804 and stretching from Fort William to Arisaig, it was the first road to be started by the Commissioners for Highland Roads and Bridges who were established the previous year. With Thomas Telford as their engineer they built hundreds of miles of roads over the next twenty years and largely established the Highland road network. As communications improved so did the prospects for businesses like the hotel sandwiched between rails and road in this early twentieth century picture. It has had a few make-overs and name changes since then.

Moidart, Glenfinnan

The area was also served by a steamer that plied the waters of Loch Shiel between Glenfinnan and Acharacle. The daily service began in 1898 when local landowners, put a yacht, *Lady of the Lake*, on the run. She was joined in 1899 by *Clanranald*, the boat seen in this picture, but she drew too much water and was replaced after less than two full seasons by *Clanranald II*, the boat seen at Acharacle on page 3. She became a favourite, not least because passengers got a free cup of tea during the journey. The service was taken over by David MacBrayne in 1953 with two new vessels, the *Lochshiel* launched in October that year and *Lochailort* which came into service the following summer. The operation continued until 1967 when the new road between Kinlochmoidart and Inverailort provided a viable alternative.

Moidart, Glenfinnan

It is possible that small scale prospecting for minerals took place in the hills to the north of Strontian before the landowner, Sir Alexander Murray of Stanhope, did some digging for himself. He promoted his discoveries of lead hoping to attract a lessee and about 1730 the York Building Company took over the workings. They set about mining on a large scale with an experienced labour force brought in from England, but pulled out after only about ten years. The mines were worked occasionally for the rest of century until 1790 when an entirely new mineral element was discovered, and named strontium after the village. The mines were working again during the Napoleonic Wars when lead bullets were made in an adjacent foundry and digging continued for a time in the nineteenth century. There was some mining in the early years of the twentieth century and the area's mineral cocktail was later exploited for barytes, for use in oil drilling muds when the North Sea oil fields created a demand. The remains of the old mines are seen here in a view looking east to the mountain, Sgurr Dhomhnuill.

Sunart, Strontian

The York Building Company accommodated their workers from south of the border at a settlement known as New York. It was only a small apple and also short-lived, but the English influence in the area appears to have continued with some of the later buildings like Horsely Hall (upper) and Kilcamb. Both of these houses became hotels, although Horsely Hall, when known as the Loch Sunart Hotel, was destroyed by a fire at Hogmanay 1998/99. The main village of Strontian, with its grassy square surrounded by trees, is sometimes also described as English, although a new housing development and village centre, built in the 1960s and 70s, has given it the more universal appearance of that period: not very English, but not very Highland either.

Sunart, Strontian

If Strontian was characterised by elements of Englishness, Scotstown, situated between the mine workings and the main village, was patently Scottish. It was a crofting community, one of three in the vicinity of Strontian, the others being the neighbouring township of Anaheilt, and Ardnastang on the shore of Loch Sunart. In 1923 the number of crofts in the area was increased when the Department of Agriculture broke up farms at Drumnatorran on the east bank of the Strontian River, Carnoch in Glen Tarbert, and Rannachan and Ardery to the west of Strontian. This use of larger farms to create smallholdings was done throughout the crofting counties to provide land for men returning from the forces after the First World War.

Sunart, Strontian

One of the biggest upheavals in Scottish social history occurred in 1843 when a dispute within the Church of Scotland led to an event known as the Disruption, when about forty per cent of ministers and a higher proportion of parishioners left the church to set up the Free Church of Scotland. The central issue was whether a powerful patron, usually a landowner, or the congregation should have the right to appoint a minister. Dissention was very high at Strontian, but the landowner refused to allow the congregation to build a new church, so they commissioned one from a shipyard on the Clyde, which is seen in this contemporary engraving being towed into Loch Sunart. It was one of the most extraordinary episodes of a troubled time, but the floating church remained in use for thirty years. It could accommodate up to 750 people and the success of a preacher could be measured by how deeply in the water the church sat: a spiritual level perhaps?

Sunart, Strontian

Kinlochaline Castle sits on a rocky outcrop at the head of Loch Aline. Possibly dating originally from the fifteenth century and subsequently modified it was described in the nineteenth century as 'a strong but rudely constructed keep'. By that time it was in a derelict state, but at the end of the century it was given a makeover to turn it into an interesting landscape feature. During this process it lost much of its appeal as a romantic ruin and is seen here in the 1950s looking somewhat squared off and uninteresting. It was restored as a home in 1999/2000, a process that also returned it to the status of a really interesting feature in the landscape. The picture also shows the bridge built in 1888 to give access to Ardtornish Estate.

Morvern, Kinlochaline

Some ten years after buying Achranich Estate in 1845 Octavius Smith built a shooting lodge on a site overlooking Loch Aline. He then acquired the neighbouring Ardtornish Estate and transferred its name to the original property. The house fell victim to dry rot and Smith's son, Thomas, had it demolished in 1884 and replaced with the mansion seen in this early twentieth century picture. It was a concrete and steel structure faced with stone, and built to the designs of architect Alexander Ross. Protruding from the trees in the left background is a campanile, a detached part of the original house. It was intended as a flue, with smoke from the house fires being ducted through it, but while that idea failed, the tower outlived the house and had the pitched roof added.

Morvern, Kinlochaline

37

To modern eyes Lochaline seems like a natural place for a settlement, yet it only came into existence in the nineteenth century when a community of evicted crofters was established in the wake of the Clearances. Initially there was little to sustain it, but it became an industrial village in 1940, during the Second World War, when the Glasgow firm of Charles Tennant & Company opened a mine for silica sand. The sand was ideal for making high quality optical glass and was needed because the war had cut off other supplies from Europe. After the war the mine remained in operation and continued to expand to provide the raw material for a range of glass-making industries. It changed hands a couple of times and closed in December 2008, although plans to reopen it were announced in 2011, so the story goes on.

Morvern, Lochaline

The boat seen here leaving Lochaline Pier is the *Lochinvar* which was specially built in 1908 for the service operated by David MacBrayne to communities on both sides of the Sound of Mull. On leaving Oban she called at Lismore, then Craignure on Mull, Lochaline, back across to Mull at Salen, then over to Morvern again at Drimnin before re-crossing the Sound of Mull to Tobermory. Kilchoan was also included during the summer months. Only the third diesel-powered MacBrayne boat, she started life with unlovely exhaust pipes and a derrick, which were later replaced with a stubby funnel and a deck crane, the arrangement that appears to be shown in this picture. An enclosed bridge and wheelhouse were added in 1949 before she was replaced in 1955. Her successors have since been superseded by the ferry that operates between Lochaline and Fishnish on Mull.

Morvern, Lochaline

In July 1921 a service of commemoration and thanksgiving was held in Keil Church where a roll of honour to the men of Morvern who served in the First World War was placed. The names of those who died were picked out in gold. After the service the large crowd followed Pipe Major John Scoular of Shielbridge to the war memorial that had been erected by an Oban contractor on a rocky knoll opposite the old Ardtornish Castle. The crowd is seen here gathering around the seventeen foot high rugged cross of Ardsheal granite, rising from a base of granite boulders. Designed by the artist D. Y. Cameron and brought to fruition by Stirling architect Eric Bell, it was unveiled by Mrs G. Craig Sellar of Ardtornish, whose husband had played a leading role in setting up the memorial.

Morvern, Lochaline

Superficially this house at Lochaline looks the same as other thatched cottages throughout the Highlands and islands, but there were significant regional variations. This one is bigger with higher walls and larger windows than houses on the Hebrides. Also, unlike the island houses, the roof overlaps the wall head, and the thatching, which is possibly made of heather or bracken, is held down by horizontal straps rather than a pattern of ropes weighted with stones. Following the Crofters Holdings (Scotland) Act of 1886, when people gained security of tenure, such buildings began to be replaced by dwellings that offered more in the way of creature comforts. That said, what could be better than to enjoy a stunning view from a sun-drenched bench beside the front door.

Morvern, Lochaline

This terrace of estate workers' cottages at Larachbeg was built of concrete to the designs of Samuel Barham in 1875. The photograph was taken in the 1930s, at the time when Larachbeg became one of the places where the people evacuated from the island of St. Kilda were housed. Once they had settled into their new homes the men started work at the new Forestry Commission plantation. It was an alien occupation for men who had never seen trees and were used to providing for themselves by crofting, fishing and catching wild sea birds. They also struggled with the concept of using money to meet their needs. The women too found it hard to adapt to a lifestyle that did not involve the hard, harsh work of crofting.

Morvern, Larachbeg

The western part of Morvern is almost made into an island by Loch Teacuis, Loch Aline, the little Loch Doire nam Mart and Loch Arienas, seen here behind a man, believed to be the Ardtornish estate gamekeeper, with his dogs. This moor and mountain landscape once sustained a number of families, but its status as an empty wilderness was ensured by men like Patrick Sellar. As the Duke of Sutherland's factor, Sellar carried out the infamous evictions from Strathnaver and other parts of the Sutherland estates. As well as making an unflattering name for himself, he made a lot of money and used it to buy land in Morvern, which he cleared of people in order to run sheep over the empty hills. By the early twentieth century, when this picture was taken, sheep farming had largely been replaced by the 'sport' of shooting wildlife.

Morvern, Loch Arienas

Ardgour is an area of mountain and moorland, with habitation clinging to a narrow coastal strip, as is shown by these pictures, shot by a photographer who barely moved from a spot beside the old road to take them. The upper picture looks west to Glen Gour with Sallachan steading and house on the right: below, the camera looks south across the River Gour to Ard Daraich and Ben Leamhain. Both views are likely to be missed by travellers because the new road has consigned this section of the old to the status of cut-off loop. It has also contrived to hide from visitors one of the glories of Telford's early nineteenth century road, the splendid double-arched bridge over the river.

Ardgour, River Gour

Many European languages have a similar word for a mill: in old Scots it is 'miln', in French 'Moulin' (think of the Moulin Rouge) and in Gealic, never a language to economise on characters, it is Mhuillinn. The pronunciation of 'mh' as 'v' also serves to disguise its common root and hide the origins of a crofting village like Clovulin. The mill no longer exists, but in this picture of the Ardgour Store, the woman on the right is leaning on a handrail fixed to a bridge over the lade. The store and adjacent house have been somewhat modified since the picture was taken. Just out of picture on the left is the Memorial Hall, erected in the 1932 and extended, with an arch over the mill lade, in 1973. The Ardgour Primary School was built on the other side of the road in the 1990s.

Ardgour, Clovulin

Ardgour Church was one of 32 churches, and 41 manses, built with funds awarded by parliament in 1824 to enable the Established Church of Scotland to extend its reach into the Highlands. Administration of the funds was delegated to the Commissioners for Highland Roads and Bridges. They passed the design and construction to their chief surveyor, Thomas Telford, who, in turn, instructed his local surveyors to draw up plans, which were modified to create a standard design and thus control costs. Known as 'parliamentary churches' one was built at Strontian, another at Acharacle while the one at Ardgour was served by a minister who also had charge of yet another such church across Loch Linnhe at North Ballachulish. His manse was at Onich.

Ardgour, Ardgour village

At Ardgour, Telford not only had some responsibility for the church, but also for designing the road that ran from here to Kinlochmoidart and improving the ferry facilities and pier seen in the foreground of this picture. In the background is the distinctive mountain Sgurr na h-Eanchainne, also known as Ben Keil. At just under 2,400 feet, it falls well short of the fabled Munro level of 3,000 feet, but has nevertheless attracted climbers for decades. Another Ardgour hill that fails on the Munro measure (as indeed they all do) is Garbh Bheinn, a peak that came to be regarded as one of the country's finest rock mountains. Composed of a roughish gneiss that provides a good hold, the precipitous eastern face, rising above Garbh Choire Mor, offers some of rock climbing's most testing routes.

Ardgour, Ardgour village

For an area that is actually part of the mainland there are more ferries serving communities from Ardnamurchan to Ardgour than operate to many islands. The principal ferry is the one at Corran, which is the vital link in the road west to Kinlochmoidart. The McLeans, who had acquired Ardgour by force from its earlier owners the MacMasters, operated the ferry up to the 1930s when it was taken over by Argyll County Council and run by them and subsequent local authorities. This picture from 1948 shows our intrepid tourists from Fife on board what appears to be one of the two-car ferries taken over by the County Council. The boats have been upgraded a number of times a since then.

Ardgour, Corran Ferry

KELLIE AND
BRAD

KELLIE AND BRAD

SUBTITLE

True love. On the rocks

FIRST EDITION 2020

CHAPTER 1

The concentration etched on her face. The strength uncoiling from her body as she powered out of the hack. The graceful follow-through as she extended her arm and let go of the rock.

The way her tight pants framed her ass as she delivered each practice shot.

Perfect. Every time.

He sighed as she delivered another rock and watched it settle into the rings, stopping right on the button. He wondered how things had come to this point in his life.

Curling was a major part of his life. He didn`t have a natural talent for the game; he was only ever good enough to play in the Sunday night beer leagues. But he was a friendly presence around the curling club, and the president appreciated his dedication enough to give him a job as a maintenance man on the grounds. He took to his position with relish, and over time he was given more responsibilities, eventually becoming the key assistant to the head icemaker.

Despite being around the game for so long, he loved it more than ever. He enjoyed the mental aspect of the sport, trying to match wits and strategy with the teams as he watched games unfold, whether it be at a local bonspiel or the championship matches on TV.

But most of all, it was the people. Curling athletes were the most down-to-earth of any sport, of that he was fully convinced. He attended several championship events and met the best players in the world, and all of them were genuinely nice, regular people. In no other sport would you see the athletes mingling so much with the fans, even having a beer with them, yet this happened in curling all the time because the whole community was so tight-knit.

He preferred to watch the women compete. Women generally relied less on sheer power and more on nuanced strategy and intricate shot-making, and he enjoyed that aspect of their game. And yes, if he was being completely honest, he found most female curlers to be very attractive. In his mind it was the perfect combination of athleticism and girl-next-door looks they possessed that he found irresistible.

But no one captured his attention more than Kellie, who was without a doubt the best curler this small town had ever produced.

Kellie usually wore her straight black hair in a ponytail when he saw her, which was nearly always at the curling club. Her brown eyes were focused and intense, and they were framed by functional yet stylish wire-rimmed glasses. This gave him a secret thrill, as he had a thing for women in glasses. Her breasts were no more than a handful, but they fit her body shape very well. Her hips flared out ever so sweetly, giving her a curvy, womanly frame that was very pleasing to his eye. He never saw her in dresses or skirts, only pants, so he didn`t have a good idea what her legs looked like when bare, but he was sure they were very strong and powerful after years in the sport.

But he thought her best feature was her ass, by far. It was tight and firm, two fleshy globes that he saw countless times when she was bent over, preparing herself to deliver yet another rock to its target. It looked great clothed, so he could only guess at how tremendous it would be in the nude. Many times when he was at home during the night, surrounded by nothing more than his own thoughts and fantasies, he asked himself if he had seen a better butt in his life. The answer was always the same. It was Kellie`s. Her ass was the best, the most rounded, the most succulent, the most desirable.

The most remarkable thing about Kellie, in his opinion, was it appeared she had no idea how sexy she was. No idea at all. If anything, that just made her more attractive to him, as if he were in on a titillating secret no one else knew about.

He thought about Kellie a lot more recently, if that was possible, and it was kind of making him crazy. He envisioned her slowly stripping her clothes and seductively walking towards him. He imagined how her legs would feel wrapped around his torso while they embraced as lovers. He wondered how soft her skin would be when he caressed her ass cheeks. He saw himself driving his...

"Brad!"

He sat up in a jerk and looked up. It was Russ, the head icemaker, his boss and, for all intents and purposes, his best friend. "Jeez, Russ, you scared me half to death! I`m sorry, did you need me..."

Russ softly chuckled and waved his hand in a dismissive though not unfriendly gesture. "It`s OK, we have some time yet." He sat down and cocked his head towards the ice. "Watching Kellie again, I see."

Brad softly nodded. "Yeah."

"You like her, don`t you?"

"God help me, I do."

Russ chuckled again. "You know, as good a curler as she is, I don`t think she`s good at mind-reading."

"What do you mean?"

"I mean, you should ask her out."

Brad bowed his head. "I don`t know, man."

"Come on, you sound like a scared grade schooler."

"What if she says no?"

"What if she says yes?

Brad sighed in exasperation. "I just... I don`t know."

Russ put a friendly hand on Brad`s shoulder. "Well, I may not know much about love, but here`s what I do know. You can`t slowly waste away pining for her, it will drive you insane. Ask her. If she says no, it will hurt but at least you`ll know where you stand. If she says yes, then... who knows?"

Brad rolled Russ`s words around in his head. He knew his friend was right, of course, but acting on his romantic desires was always something he struggled with. He watched Kellie make another practice shot, thinking about recent well-publicized events in her professional curling life.

He thought she could use some moral support and some love. The more he thought about it, the more he wanted to be that source of support and love. He also thought if the time was not right now, it never would be.

Finally he said, "You know Russ, you`re right. I will ask her."

"Good for you! You`d better get down there, her practice ends in 5 minutes."

"But what about work?"

"Don`t worry. I can handle things the rest of the afternoon, there isn`t that much left to do. Now go on, Brad, before you get cold feet!"

Brad shook his friend`s hand and patted him on the back. "Thanks Russ," he said. Then he left the lounge/observation area and hurried towards the ice.

****

She knew he watched her.

If it were anyone else, she was pretty sure she would be entirely creeped out. Somehow, though, he was different. He seemed completely without guile or hidden agenda, and his intentions seemed pure; he was just a regular guy who loved the sport as much as she did and wanted to be around it as much as he could. He was friendly and very well-liked and respected by all at the curling club, as well as by the townspeople at large.

And, if she were being completely honest, she found him to be a very good-looking man.

He was big and strong, years of physical labour toning his body. He had a square jaw, a barrel chest and broad shoulders. She thought about what it would be like to run her hands over his muscular frame. His face and demeanour were welcoming and friendly, and he was always nothing but a perfect gentleman towards her. Still, she sensed his face, and particularly his deep blue eyes, held more than a hint of mystery. She often wondered what thoughts lie behind those eyes.

Despite her thoughts of him, and the realization that, at least on some level, he held more than a passing interest in her, she never even considered the possibility he might be interested in a more intimate relationship with her. She never thought he would think of her as sexy. Why would he, she often thought. She never thought of herself as attractive so it didn`t occur to her that others might.

It was but one negative aspect of her life that, on the whole, she could feel crumble around her. Her day job was uninspiring. She had few friends outside of curling. In fact, other than on a sheet of curling ice, there wasn`t one area of her life in which she had any real satisfaction or confidence. Damn her unhappy childhood, she often thought when contemplating her fate.

Kellie`s parents divorced when she was young, and she shuttled between her father, who preferred her hockey-playing older brother, and her mother, who doted on her princess of a younger sister. She made few friends in her big-city grade school and was often teased and bullied by other girls. When offered the chance to move to the small town, with an aunt and uncle, to start high school, she jumped at it immediately, eager for a new start.

But she had a lot of trouble adjusting to the rhythms of small-town life, and her aunt and uncle did not provide a nurturing household, leaving her alone to deal with her own issues and insecurities surrounding boys, body image, and other typical teenage obsessions. She had few dates. She did have one boyfriend to whom she did lose her virginity. But the boy was selfish, more interested in his needs than hers, making it for her a fumbling, humiliating experience.

Being introduced to curling in her first year of high school was her saving grace, the only place she felt she belonged. She had a natural talent for the game which the coaches saw and developed in her. Otherwise feeling like a fish out of water, she found the curling club to be a true sanctuary for her. But as she grew into a woman and continued in the game, even that feeling started to desert her.

Kellie was developing a reputation as a "nearly woman" in the game. She lost in many semi-final and final matches in her junior days, and the pattern continued when she turned professional. She lost the provincial finals to the same team three times running. Last year she did win provincials, but only because her nemesis took the year off from the sport to help raise her family. Her team got hot at nationals and reached the semi-final, but she failed in her last shot and her team lost in heartbreaking fashion. Those in the know said she could never "win the big one". Her team was in turmoil; she managed to hold them together for now but she wondered for how long. She practiced obsessively for the upcoming season, but the pressure she put on herself to win was enormous, and it was starting to suck the joy out of the game for her. She cried many nights wondering if she could cope.

All these thoughts were swirling through her head after she finished practice. She was so distracted she did not see Brad waiting at the hallway entrance; she nearly literally bowled him over.

"Oh god, I`m sorry Brad! Are you OK? Oh I didn`t even see you there!" Kellie said.

Brad smiled and straightened himself out. "It`s alright, Kellie. No harm done. I imagine you have a lot on your mind right now."

"Yeah", she said, but did not elaborate.

"Did practice go well?"

"Pretty good, I feel I`m throwing well. How is work around the club?"

"Oh, busy as usual. You know how it is, always something to fix."

Kellie and Brad both nodded. An uncomfortable silence hung between them. Then Kellie said, "Well, I should really get going. It was nice talking to you Brad."

With that, she headed for the change room, and Brad saw his chance slipping away. Just as Kellie pulled on the door, he yelled, "Kellie, wait!"

Even from a distance Brad could see the look of shock on her face. "Is something wrong?" she asked.

"No, no, not at all," he laughed nervously. "I... I was just wondering, are you busy tonight?"

Kellie paused, wondering where Brad was going with this. "No, I`m free tonight. Why do you ask?"

"I thought maybe you and I could go out for dinner. What do you think?"

Kellie was not expecting Brad to make such a request, but she was flattered by the interest. Saying yes went against her natural instincts. Then again, it isn`t every day a man asks you on a date, Kellie thought to herself. What the heck, it might be fun.

She smiled; it was enough to melt Brad`s heart. "Sure," she said. "I`d like that."

Brad visibly exhaled. "Great! Meet you at the diner at 7:00?"

"Sure. See you then."

Kellie went to the change room. Brad left for home to get ready, with an extra little hop in his step.

****

They were incredibly nervous.

Kellie had competed in big curling matches, watched in arenas by thousands and on TV by millions, yet she was more nervous for this date than anything she had experienced before in her life. She nearly called Brad five different times to cancel. She even considered just not showing up but realized that would heartlessly crush Brad, and she desperately did not want to do that to such a sweet guy. She changed outfits several times, finally settling on a pretty floral dress that fit her well without being too revealing. A white pair of medium heels completed the ensemble. After taking several deep breaths, she finally felt ready to go.

Brad hadn`t fared much better in his preparations. He was so anxious he threw up soon after he got home. He finally felt well enough to shower and get ready. He shaved and prepped himself about as much as a man could before going out on a first date. Deciding on his best collared dress shirt and pair of khaki pants, he left his house hoping he would make a good impression on Kellie. He picked up a small, simple floral arrangement at the general store before getting to the diner, trusting Kellie would appreciate the gesture.

He reached the diner fifteen minutes early. He was restless, pacing back and forth. Meanwhile, she realized she would be late if she didn`t hurry up. She walked as fast as she could in her heels, all the while doubt creeping in whether he`d even be there at all, making her the butt of yet another cruel cosmic joke.

Brad saw Kellie first as she rounded the street corner. With her wearing a dress and a nicely coiffed hairdo, he almost didn`t recognize her at first. But once he knew it was her he was captivated all over again by just how pretty she was. His heartbeat accelerated as she got closer and closer.

Kellie was touched to see Brad holding flowers for her, a perfectly gentlemanly thing to do. She also couldn`t help but notice him shuffling his feet from side to side like a skittish five year-old. I`m glad I`m not the only one who`s nervous as hell, she thought.

They were both smiling at each other as Kellie stopped in front of Brad.

"Hi Kellie," said Brad.

"Hi Brad," replied Kellie.

Still smiling, time standing still, neither of them moved.

Finally Brad shook his head. "Sorry, kind of zoned out there for a second... these are for you."

"Thank you, that`s very sweet. They are pretty." Kellie gave him a small kiss on the cheek.

"Thanks, you`re pretty too."

Kellie smiled and blushed but said nothing.

Brad held out his arm. "Shall we?"

Kellie held him by the elbow and answered, "I`d like that."

They entered the diner and were given a semi-private booth in the back corner. They couldn`t help but notice the other patrons, most of them regulars, watching them as they took their seats. It made Kellie a little self-conscious, but Brad only thought, let them look, I`m with the prettiest girl around and I don`t care who knows it.

It turned out to be a wonderful dinner. It took a few awkward moments to break the ice, but before long they made each other at ease and enjoyed a stimulating conversation. Kellie in particular felt disarmed by Brad; he was funny and interesting, but more importantly was a good listener. She quickly found herself comfortable enough to tell him much of her life story, including things she shared with few other people.

For his part Brad was sympathetic to Kellie`s situation. He was more impressed with her accomplishments than ever, given the challenges she had to overcome. More than anything else though he knew he was falling deeply and madly in love with Kellie.

They talked well into the night. The sun set outside, all the other customers left long ago, and the diner employees were cleaning up around them, yet still they talked and laughed and enjoyed each other`s company. Kellie saw the clock read 11:00 pm, looked around and said, "I think they`re going to kick us out of here soon."

Brad sighed and said, "Yeah, I guess we should let them lock up for the night."

They went outside, hand in hand, into the brisk, early spring night. They walked for a few minutes in a pleasant silence.

"Thank you so much Brad, I had a wonderful time tonight."

"So did I Kellie. I hope we can do it again real soon."

He leaned in towards her face. She tilted her head to accept him. Slowly, gently, they kissed.

They agreed to see each other again soon before parting ways for the evening.

Kellie returned home in a state of turmoil. She`d had a marvellous time, but was still conflicted over her emotions. She wasn`t used to being in a close relationship, and the thought that she could find herself in one so quickly kind of scared her. She worried that something that was starting so well could only end badly. She ended up crying herself to sleep.

Brad went home walking on a cloud. He was grinning like an idiot the whole way, not that he cared. He kissed Kellie Ferguson, and it felt wonderful.

****

They went out again the next night.

And again the next night. And the night after that.

Pretty soon they were a regular item. The consensus among the townsfolk was that they made a cute couple.

Brad was thrilled that Kellie seemed to like him so much. The last six months when they were together were the happiest he`d ever had. He hoped the relationship could progress into something more intimate, because he longed to do more with Kellie than just chaste kissing. He wanted to touch and taste her, all of her. But he understood that she was fragile, and he did not want to jeopardize what he felt was a very special relationship. So he was fine with taking things slow for now, hoping to break Kellie out of her shell.

Kellie felt safe with Brad. She loved the sound of his laugh, the smell of his after-shave and the strong and protective grip he exerted when they held hands. She was still worried though, because she figured Brad would eventually want a more physical side to their relationship, and she wasn`t sure if she could handle that yet. She also agonized over the possibility that Brad would ultimately reject her, even though it seemed ridiculous because it was not in his nature to be cruel.

It was a glorious late summer evening. They were having a picnic in the park. Their conversation, as it often did, turned to curling.

"I have a good feeling about your team this year, Kellie," said Brad. "Your two front-end players are improving all the time, your vice-skip is strong, and, well, of course you`re an amazing curler. You`ll win provincials again, for sure. I can feel it."

"I don`t know," replied Kellie. "The Morriss team is back again. I just can`t seem to beat them."

"Sure you can. They are good, but you`re better. You just have to believe."

"You say it like it`s so easy."

"Well, I can only imagine it`s not easy, even for a naturally gifted curler such as yourself." Kellie couldn`t help but blush at Brad`s praise.

"But," Brad continued, "you won last year, and you almost won nationals, and there were some very strong teams there. You can win. You will win."

"I`m not sure. A lot of people say I can`t win when it counts the most."

"Says who?"

"People in the big city, in the media..."

"Them?" Brad scoffed. "Forget them. They have no idea what they are talking about. The people in this town say you can win." He gently held Kellie`s face in his hands. "I say you can win."

Kellie smiled but said nothing. Brad noticed sadness in her eyes.

"You`re not used to this, are you?"

"Not used to what?"

"Positive reinforcement."

Kellie sighed. "Not so much, I guess. My coaches and teammates try but what they say doesn`t seem to stick. And I never got a lot of it growing up, as I`ve told you before. I`m not sure that I`ve earned your confidence in me."

"Well, trust me, Kellie, you do deserve to have people believe in you. And you will need to get used to it, because I`ll always support you, whether you want me to or not."

"Thanks Brad, that`s very sweet of you."

They kissed and lay back in the cool grass, holding hands, watching the sunset. After the sun went down they decided to leave, and as they were getting up, Brad said, "If I`m not being too forward, I`d love for you to come back to my place for some coffee."

Kellie felt butterflies in the pit of her stomach. She wasn`t sure about this. But Brad was always so nice to her, especially tonight, and coffee sounded harmless. She finally said, "OK. Coffee. I`d like that."

Brad smiled and took Kellie`s hand. They walked back to his house. Kellie noticed it was modest but very well-maintained from the outside, and while there was some evidence of a bachelor lifestyle inside it was still tidy. She sat down in the living room as Brad went to work brewing some coffee. Again she was nearly overcome with anxiety. She wanted to make Brad happy but genuinely didn`t know how.

Brad inhaled the warm aroma of the coffee. He was thrilled Kellie decided to come to his house, but he knew he still had to walk a fine line balancing his desires and the precarious nature of her state of mind. He thought he could help, though. Just being with Kellie for these six months had done wonders for his own confidence, and in his mind he believed he could do the same for her. He came up with a plan as the coffee brewed. It was a little hokey, he thought, but it just might work.

He walked to the living room and gave Kellie her mug. They sat on the couch together, quietly drinking their coffee. Kellie watched Brad as he fished into his pocket and pulled out a shiny new penny. He took the penny and placed it in her hand, folding her fingers over it.

"Brad? What`s this?" she asked.

"For your thoughts."

"I`m sorry?"

"You know. A penny. For your thoughts."

Kellie couldn`t help but laugh a little. It was so corny, but also so... Brad. But she quickly turned serious, realizing this was probably his gentle way to ask her to open up to him, to have the "where is this relationship going" talk. She took a deep breath in a futile effort to quell the butterflies. When she finally did speak, her voice was thin and shaky.

"Brad, you`ve been so wonderful to me. You make me smile and laugh, and you make me feel special. No one`s ever been so nice to me, and I`ve never felt this way with anyone else before."

"Thank you, Kellie. It makes me very happy to hear you say that."

"I... I just have one question."

"Shoot."

"Why?"

Brad was confused. "I`m... not sure what you mean by that."

"Why me? Why take all your time and energy on me? I don`t know what I`ve done to deserve this."

Brad didn`t react at first. Then a small smile crept on to one corner of his face, spreading until eventually he was positively beaming.

"What`s with the smile?" Kellie asked.

"You really don`t know, do you?"

Kellie was becoming a little annoyed by his reaction. "Bradley Galenchuk," she said, using his full name, "stop with the teasing and explain yourself!"

It felt like the moment of truth for Brad, and he decided to jump in head-first. He leaned forward and kissed Kellie, as he had done many times before, except this time he let one of his hands wander down to her rear end and gave it a little squeeze. She flinched in surprise, while he just looked in her eyes and said "You don`t know just how beautiful a person you are, and you don`t know just how much of an effect you have on me with how sexy you are!"

Kellie just bowed her head and said nothing.

"Kellie... what`s wrong?"

"Do you really mean what you just said? I just find it difficult to believe you could really feel that way about me, or that I am in any way worthy of your affection."

"Yes, you are. I can. And I do."

Kellie fell silent again, paralyzed by her inability to accept Brad`s apparent love for her.

Brad closed his eyes and took a deep breath. This was proving to be more difficult than he thought. He understood on some level that Kellie had low self-esteem but he underestimated just how bad it was. He was not about to give up, however; if anything it made him more determined. He also realized he couldn`t show any of the frustration he was feeling, otherwise he knew he`d lose her forever. He smiled, stood up and extended his hand to Kellie.

"I want to show you something, Kellie. Please," he said.

Kellie sighed. "What is it?"

"Do you trust me?"

"I beg your pardon?"

"Do you trust me?"

"I... I... yes."

"Good. Then come with me."

Kellie stood up, wanting to fully trust Brad but still wary of what his endgame was. She held his hand and he led her to a hallway, stopping just outside his bedroom door in front of a full-length mirror, where he stood behind her, holding her gently around her waist.

"Now," Brad said, trying to keep his voice soft and kind, "take a good look in the mirror. Tell me, what do you see?"

"You and I standing in front of a mirror. Brad, what are you..."

"No Kellie, I mean look closely. REALLY look. Humour me. Please."

Kellie sighed and said, "OK, I`ll play along."

Brad gave her shoulders an affectionate squeeze. "Thank you, I promise it will be worth it. Now, what do you see when you look at yourself in the mirror?"

"Could I start by describing what I see when I look at you?" Kellie asked.

Brad briefly considered this and then smiled and nodded his head yes.

"OK. I see a strong, handsome man. I see a perfect gentleman, someone I`ve never heard say a bad word towards anyone. I see a man with a big laugh and a goofy sense of humour. And I see a man who is completely crazy for wanting to spend so much time with me."

Brad started to plant little kisses on Kellie`s neck, earlobes and shoulder blades. A soft gasp escaped Kellie`s mouth. When Brad spoke, his voice was deep, guttural and more than a little hungry.

"I assure you, my dear Kellie, I am 100% sane. But in a way, I guess I am crazy... crazy in love. Want to know why? Because of the woman I see in the mirror. I see a woman who is athletic and dedicated. I see an intelligent woman, smart enough to succeed at a mentally demanding sport and lead a team to greatness along the way. I see a woman who has overcome many challenges in her life to become a successful and genuinely good person. I see a woman who, as great as she is, could be even greater if she would just believe in herself and allow others to believe in her too. I see a woman who has both tremendous inner and tremendous outer beauty."

Kellie`s eyes turned hazy and dreamy. Brad`s voice put her into an almost-trance, and his words touched her heart in ways no one had ever done. A single tear rolled down her cheek, which he softly wiped away with his hand.

"One more thing," Brad said.

Kellie cocked her eyebrow, silently asking him to go on. He turned her almost all the way to face him and then adjusted her head so she could look at her backside`s reflection.

"I see a woman who has the finest, firmest ass a man could ever dream of!" Brad growled.

Kellie`s eyes grew wide, and to her surprise she felt a naughty little smile form on her lips. "Bradley Galenchuk, are you getting fresh with me?"

"Maybe," he playfully teased.

Kellie stayed in the position she was in, her eyes darting back and forth between the reflection of her rear end in the mirror and Brad, whose eyes she could see locked on to her butt. "You really think I have a nice ass?" she asked.

"Not just nice, Kellie. Amazing," was his reply.

She stared back at her reflection, studying it, as if she were truly seeing it for the first time. She wore jeans that, she had to admit, did cling to her hips and butt quite nicely. She bent over a few inches and wiggled her rear end ever so slightly, a sight that caused Brad`s mouth to open and his manhood to surge forward.

"Not bad," Kellie purred.

Brad gave a silent prayer of thanks. Those two words alone represented a major victory in helping Kellie overcome her poor self-esteem. Surely it was the start of greater things to come.

Kellie felt flush in her cheeks, but that warmth held nothing on the inferno she felt down below in her sex. She turned around, guided Brad`s hands onto her ass, and then very firmly grabbed his butt cheeks. She kissed him with more hunger and fire than she ever had before. Their tongues parted each other`s lips and danced together. After coming up for air Kellie panted, "Brad, I want to please you. I want you to please me. Show me how."

Brad was filled with desire, his erection desperate to be freed from his pants. "Just follow my lead, baby, and tell me what feels good to you. I promise I won`t do anything you don`t want to do, but please let me make sweet love to you."

In a very bold move for her, she let her hands travel to his crotch and rubbed it, feeling his impressive hardness. "Yes, baby, that`s what I want, show me what a real man can do!"

Brad led Kellie the short distance to his bedroom, kissing her the whole way. He carefully undressed her, and she was happy to let him do it. Kellie was still very nervous but she understood deep down this was something she both needed and wanted very badly, and she reasoned if Brad was as tender and loving with sex as he was with every other part of their relationship then things would be fine. She was now naked before him, and did not attempt to cover up. He took a minute to admire her beauty. "God, you`re stunning!" he exclaimed, and then started to undress himself.

"Not so fast. Allow me," Kellie said. She removed Brad`s shirt and ran her hands down his muscular chest and defined abs, stopping only when they reached his belt buckle. She undid the belt and pulled off his pants and boxers in one movement. She chewed on her lower lip as she gazed on his long and thick erection, wanting to discover how he would use his tool to pleasure her body.

Brad guided Kellie to stand up again. He stepped in close and inhaled deeply, enthralled by the scent of her feminine arousal. He kissed her from her earlobe down to the tops of her breasts. He took both of them in his hands, two perfect handfuls that fit just right. He flicked the left nipple while he kissed and nibbled at the right. Kellie moaned "Yes!" as she felt currents of electricity surge to her erogenous zones as a result of Brad`s touch.

After a few minutes of loving attention on her breasts Brad trailed his tongue all the way down Kellie`s flat stomach. He turned her around and bent her over at the waist so she faced the foot of his bed, giving him his first full view of both her naked vagina and ass. "Oh god, so beautiful," he said, and his soft breath raised goose bumps on her soft milky-white flesh. He massaged her cheeks and planted little butterfly kisses on her inner thighs, moving closer and closer to her exposed sex. It was a sweet torture for her; she loved the softness and care he was giving but she was eager for more.

He reached her treasure spot. The room was heady with her musky aroma. He licked up and down her opening and probed her lips and folds. This caused her to buck a little and exclaim, "Oh my god!" He rubbed her mound and licked her, then penetrated her with his tongue.

Given her relative sexual inexperience, there was no way for her to properly describe it, but she felt something powerful build deep within her. Her breaths became shallow and ragged. The pleasure was almost too enormous to comprehend. Then he found her clitoris, peeking out of her like a love bud. His flicking and bathing it with his tongue sent her crashing over the edge.

"Yes Brad, YES YES YES!!!" Kellie screamed in ecstasy as she climaxed. Wave after wave of her juices drenched his face and the sheets at the edge of the bed. Her knees shook and buckled, and she collapsed on the bed. It was her first real orgasm given to her by someone else, and she was a little shocked by its intensity.

Brad delicately traced his hands along her legs and buttocks as she recovered from her contact high. He went to the head of the bed and looked into her eyes. "So, I take it you enjoyed that?" he asked.

Kellie didn`t say anything but looked up at Brad and smiled. Then in a flash she leapt off the bed and jumped into Brad`s arms, knocking him flat on his back and straddling him. They kissed passionately.

"That was so amazing. No one`s ever made me feel that way," she said between kisses.

"There`s more we can do, if you`re up for it."

Kellie reached down and took hold of Brad`s stiff member, giving it several sensual strokes. "You`re so big and so hard."

"Oh god Kellie, that feels amazing!" Brad sighed in pleasure. His urge to cum was strong but he concentrated on holding back, desperately wanting to please her more.

After a few more strokes Kellie asked in a sweet, sexy voice, "Please put this inside me?"

"I`d love nothing more."

He rolled over on top of her. He lined his hard penis up to her slit, still glistening with wetness. He entered her slowly, giving her some time to adjust to his girth.

"Oh god, it`s so big! I feel so full!" she yelled.

"Are you OK? Should I stop?" He was suddenly concerned.

"NO! Please don`t stop. Do me hard. Please."

Brad smoothly plunged his rod in and out of her, slowly at first but soon picking up speed. Before long she was matching his thrusts with those of her own. Their bodies were covered in a light sheen of sweat. Her legs clenched around him in a vise-like grip, and he couldn`t help but think that, yes, they were as strong as he imagined they would be.

"Oh god Kellie, you feel so wonderfully tight! You`re going to make me come soon!" Brad exclaimed.

"Yes Brad! I`m going to come too! Make me your lover!" Kellie replied. She soon let out other screams of joy as her climax took over. He came soon after, grunting ecstatically as his ejaculation erupted inside of her.

They lay down on their sides, each holding and caressing each other, looking at each other in a contented silence, happy to do no more than bask in the afterglow.

Brad was the first to break the silence. "Thank you. For everything."

Kellie shook her head. "No, it is me who should be thanking you."

"I love you, Kellie Ferguson."

"And I love you, Bradley Galenchuk."

They drifted off into a blissful sleep.

****

FIVE MONTHS LATER

A lot can change in just one year.

If there was one coherent thought she had in the pandemonium surrounding her, that was it.

Brad gave Kellie new life. Of that, she was certain. It was not an overnight process; there were still some struggles and times when she doubted herself.

But overall Brad had a hugely positive impact on her life. He gave her plenty of encouragement and praise. He gave her support and a shoulder to cry on when she was experiencing difficulties. And yes, he was great in bed; they had many more nights of wonderful sex since first consummating their relationship. Most of all, he loved her completely and unreservedly.

The resulting change in her demeanour was clear for all to see. The townspeople noticed. More importantly, her coaches and teammates noticed. She was more consistent on the ice. She had a better command of the team and improved her ability to draw out their best performances. More importantly, she became better friends with her team. They all trusted each other more. For the first time in a while, Kellie felt she was part of a real team, and her love of curling was rekindled.

Brad was proud of Kellie`s progress. He marveled at the changes he saw, how she became more confident, more outgoing, more comfortable in her own skin. As was his way, he downplayed his role in this process. To anyone that would listen, he would say Kellie had this greatness in her, all he did was give her a nudge in the right direction to allow her to shine.

Kellie and her team certainly shone on the curling ice. They won two warm-up events and established themselves as a team to be reckoned with. They cruised through provincials and reached the finals, where, once again, Kellie met her rival. This time, the outcome was different.

Kellie and her team played flawlessly and easily defeated her nemesis. For the second year in a row, they were going to the national championship, but this win was so much more rewarding for everyone.

The town held a special banquet to congratulate the team and wish them well at nationals. There were speeches by the mayor and the president of the curling club. Brad also gave a brief but touching speech, at the end of which he surprised Kellie by presenting her with a small box. Kellie opened it to reveal a stunning diamond engagement ring. She looked up to see Brad bent on one knee before her, asking for her hand in marriage. She was overjoyed, and enthusiastically said yes. They kissed as everyone in attendance gave the newly engaged couple a standing ovation.

Kellie`s team arrived at nationals filled with confidence and eager to test themselves against the best teams in the country. They had a successful week, finishing second during the round-robin portion of the tournament, qualified for the playoffs and made their way into the championship game.

The final game was tense and thrilling. Both teams were on top of their game, making several great shots. It came down to the last shot of the final end, with the score tied. Kellie held the rock, taking a deep breath, preparing herself to make the most important shot of her career. Brad was in the large crowd watching, his stomach tied up in knots, silently praying she could pull this off.

Her form was perfect.

With perfect line calling by her third and expert sweeping by her two front-end players, Kellie delivered the rock right to the button, scoring the winning point. Kellie and her team won the national championships.

The crowd cheered loudly as Kellie and her team celebrated their achievement. While the other players looked for their loved ones in the crowd, Kellie searched frantically for Brad. She saw him running down the arena stairs toward the ice and ran to meet him. She jumped into his arms and hugged him fiercely. Several photographers and TV cameras moved in close to film the moment.

Brad thought, let them look, my fiancée is the national champion and I love her.

"You did it Kellie!" he yelled over and over, struggling to make himself heard over the din of the crowd.

"Thank you Brad, I couldn`t have done this without you!" she replied.

"I love you, Bradley Galenchuk."

"And I love you, Kellie Ferguson." He punctuated that by firmly yet lovingly swatting her ass. "Now go get that trophy!"

They kissed deeply, both more madly in love with each other than ever before.

CHAPTER 2

She seethed in anger, again.

Anita Morriss had just pressed play on her remote control. She had already watched her DVD copy of the local access cable channel`s broadcast of last year`s provincial curling finals, during which she suffered the heaviest defeat of her professional career, more times than she cared to count. Yet here she was watching it again. She heard the announcers say how much her team had defeated Kellie Ferguson`s team over the years, and she couldn`t help but shake her head at just how different the outcome was that time around.

As difficult as it was for Anita to accept losing at all, never mind to a team from some Podunk little town she thoroughly dominated many times before, there were many reasons for the loss that she could rationalize in her mind, if she wanted to. Kellie and her team were just on that day. Anita`s team did not play well, herself included. They were probably overconfident, having beaten Kellie so often in the past. Sometimes the old law of averages just catches up to you. Just one of those days, really.

Except, none of them satisfied Anita. There was something else going on, maybe just under the surface, but it was there nonetheless.

Not that she thought Kellie cheated. That was impossible. The game and its competitors were too honest for that, though Anita wasn`t above playing some old-fashioned mind games to help gain a competitive edge. Besides, even if subtle cheating had any sort of "wink-wink" acceptance in curling, Kellie was far too naïve and clueless to do anything like that.

Perhaps it was better training, new coaching, something along those lines. Wrong again, Anita thought. Her information gathering network would have gone into overdrive if that happened. Her coaches and extended support group kept track of all her main competition; they charted everything about their training, their strategy, their coaches... anything and everything having to do with how they played the game. If one of them sneezed during a training session, Anita knew about it.

So while she knew Kellie`s team had played well leading into provincials, better than they had before, she also believed it was insufficient explanation for what happened that day. And no matter how often she watched this DVD, no matter how often she thought about what that missing element was, she had not yet discovered the answer. And that bothered her in a way nothing else ever had.

Anita fast-forwarded through much of the actual match play, stopping only where she thought she might see something that would solve her problem. As of yet she had gained no new insights. She continued fast-forwarding to the end. Usually she would shut it off at this point, often so angry she wanted to throw something across the room. But this time she kept watching, thinking there might be something, anything, that she could learn.

She watched the camera focus on the Ferguson team celebrating, the perfunctory handshakes her own team exchanged with theirs, their moving to the stands, all of them appearing to embrace loved ones...

Wait.

Anita`s eyebrow raised up as she paused the DVD. As far as she knew, Kellie was single and had a difficult relationship with her family; they rarely if ever attended her matches. So if there was a special new person in Kellie`s life, this would be an unexpected development. She wondered why she didn`t notice it then, and then thought back to the anger and bitterness she tried to suppress at that time. No, Kellie could have stripped naked right there on the ice, and Anita would not have taken notice, so consumed with the defeat she was.

Now, however, she realized this could be the final piece of the puzzle she was looking to solve.

She stopped the DVD and ejected it from the player, and went to her computer to view it on her monitor. She fast-forwarded to the same point, hit pause and took a screen grab picture of that frame. She zoomed in the left corner, where Kellie was hugging somebody. The picture quality was fairly poor, but she could tell it was a man Kellie was with. He looked around her own age, and appeared to be reasonably handsome.

In order to confirm her growing suspicions, Anita went to the stack of DVDs she kept next to her TV, and pulled one which was still unopened. Her coach had written on the packaging, "Watch this, for motivation for next year!", but she had left the package alone. She knew Kellie`s team had won the Canadian title as well, but she could not stomach to watch even a second of that tournament.

And, technically, she still wouldn`t. For what she was interested in was not the game itself, but the celebration afterward.

Anita fast-forwarded this DVD until she found what she was looking for. The professional camera work was much sharper than what the volunteers with ancient equipment could provide. So there was no doubt this time that Kellie`s celebratory embrace was with an attractive, muscular man.

"Huh, amazing," Anita said out loud to no one in particular. "That nerd Kellie managed to snag herself a man!"

And that had to be the answer, didn`t it? Anita knew from personal experience that when she was getting some action in the sack, everything else in her life was much better. While she was, for now, happily single, she had achieved more than her fair share of sexual conquests; men could never resist her blonde hair and blue eyes, her tight yet curvy body, nor her assertive (to the point of being aggressive) sexuality. In between these "trophies", she had no shortage of "friends-with-benefits" when she needed to scratch that itch.

Anita breathed a sigh of relief. It wouldn`t erase the past, of course, but there was at least a small slice of bitter satisfaction at having cracked the proverbial code. She sat back on her couch, deep in thought.

She knew this coming season would be pivotal in her curling career. It had been two years since she had been to the national finals. The first year she had to take time off from the game so she and her mother could help her sister, who was seriously injured in a car accident, raise her spoiled brat of a son. And, of course, there was last season`s debacle. So motivation was definitely not an issue. She would train and practice harder than ever, and she would drive her team to do the same. She would increase her film work on her competitors, and meet more with her various coaches to go over every possible strategic detail she could encounter.

Even with her control-freak tendencies, however, Anita knew that there were some things she could not make bend to her will. If Kellie Ferguson really did have a boyfriend, and if that really did help make her, and by extension her team, become a more formidable curling rink, there wasn`t anything Anita Morriss could do about it.

Unless...

******

They were deeply in love.

The past 18 months had been a whirlwind for Kellie. Brad`s courtship of her was sweet, like everything else about him, and his support and love for her helped her become a happier, more confident person. Without him, she was convinced there would have been no way she could be the kind of player and skip needed to lead her curling team to win the Canadian championship. It was the best period of her life in every possible way, and in truth it wasn`t even close.

The same kinds of feelings held true for Brad. Though he did not have the level of personal challenges over which Kellie had to rise, he did have the sense that his life was drifting away from him before he took a chance and asked her out for their first date. No longer; now it had structure and purpose, he had a reason to get up each and every morning and be the best he could be.

They had both found their best friend, their lover, their soul mate. Someone to share life`s highs, someone to lean on for support during its lows. They talked plenty about curling, but they also spent a lot of time talking about other things. Getting married. What their future might hold. Current events, and love and life in general.

Kellie and Brad expressed their love for each other in many ways. They said I love you to each other often. They made other simple gestures, like Brad holding doors open for Kellie and other such acts of chivalry, and Kellie helping to straighten Brad`s tie when they were going out for a fancy night out, and other such caring touches. They held hands in public almost constantly. Certainly anyone who saw them together could see how much they loved each other.

And, of course, they also spent many nights making sweet, passionate love to each other. They enjoyed the process that all new lovers go through of exploring each other`s bodies, finding out what the other likes, what turns them on. Kellie loved running her soft hands over Brad`s powerfully muscled chest, and thrilled to feel his strong hands touching her all over. Brad loved how Kellie sighed blissfully when he gently nibbled on her earlobes, and of course took every opportunity he could to touch her ass, marvelling at how perfectly each cheek felt in his hands.

There was no doubt Kellie and Brad were deeply, madly in love with each other. They were absolutely convinced that, while there would be difficulties from time to time as life intruded, there was absolutely nothing that could stop this most perfect love.

Right?

******

It all started so innocently.

The late summer sun was powerful in the sky, and the heat and humidity hung heavy in the air. It was one of those days that you broke into a serious sweat just thinking about moving, Brad thought to himself. He was returning home after another hard day`s work. The curling club was embarking on a major maintenance program, so Brad`s days were extremely busy, both in helping Russ to oversee the project and in rolling up his sleeves to take part in some good old-fashioned manual labour. He was returning to an empty house for now, as Kellie was at a training session with her teammates and wouldn`t be home for another couple of hours. He looked forward to doing little more than grabbing a quick sandwich and an ice-cold beer and moving as little as possible until it was time to sleep.

He walked up to the front porch of the modest house he and Kellie now shared. He opened the mailbox and pulled out a couple of official-looking envelopes. Probably just bills, he sighed. He went to unlock the front door and go inside when something on the patio table caught his eye.

It was an oddly-shaped package, wrapped in festively-coloured paper. This was curious, Brad thought to himself. No one he knew would be sending any special deliveries to himself or Kellie. Would they? Very curious indeed.

Brad brought everything inside and pulled a beer from the fridge. He took two long, satisfying pulls from the bottle, savouring the taste and coldness of the alcoholic beverage. His immediate thirst quenched for now, he returned his attention to the peculiar package. He took the card that was stapled to the top of the package. It read, simply, in a standard typing font, "To Brad". Nothing else was on the card; no indication who it was from, no return address, nothing.

Even more curious, he opened the package, and revealed a miniature flowering bonsai tree. It wasn`t what he expected, but then again what would he expect in the first place from such a mysterious delivery? He picked it up and studied it. It looked nice enough, and was a lot less "girly" than a gift of flowers, for example. He smiled, thinking that it could only be Kellie teasing him with some elaborate plan that would lead to a romantic, maybe even sexual, evening. He gave the plant a little water and left it on the dining room table, quickly preparing himself a sandwich before returning to the couch to eat and drink the rest of his beer.

He planned to thank Kellie for the thoughtful gift, but by the time Kellie got home and they got to talking about each other`s day, he forgot all about the plant.

He didn`t think to mention it to Kellie until one week later, when he returned home from work and found another package waiting for him. Brad wondered just what Kellie`s plan was. Like the first delivery, this package had a card reading "To Brad," but nothing more. Curious-er and curious-er, Brad thought.

He knew Kellie had curling practice and would be home late, so again he could open this package without interruption. He opened the plain box, and this time found an oversized silver old-fashioned key. He inspected it closely and found some engraving on it; it read, "Brad, you hold the key to my heart!"

He smiled and shook his head, wondering what Kellie would think of next.

When Kellie returned home, Brad leapt off his chair. He playfully grabbed her, lifted her up off the ground and delivered a deep, long and passionate kiss.

"Well hello to you too, Brad!" Kellie exclaimed, laughing and still slightly out of breath. "What`s gotten into you?"

Brad hugged Kellie tightly and said, "I love you Kellie."

"I love you too Brad!"

"I just wanted to thank you and show my appreciation for the gifts you got me."

Kellie`s brow furrowed. "I`m sorry, what did you say?"

"Thank you for the gifts."

"What gifts?"

Brad looked slightly incredulous. "What do you mean, what gifts?"

"Bradley Galenchuk, what on earth are you talking about?!"

Brad recognized the tone of Kellie`s voice. She usually only used the combination of that particular tone of exasperation and saying his full name when she was either annoyed with him, or just pretending to be. He figured, correctly, that this time it wasn`t the latter. He asked Kellie to wait a minute and went into the dining room where he collected both of the items delivered to their house.

Kellie watched Brad retreat and return with a small plant and a shiny silver object. He handed them to her and she heard him say, "The bonsai tree came last week, the key was delivered today."

She looked at them both carefully. "I wondered what the heck this plant was," she said. She then raised an eyebrow when she read the engraving on the key.

Brad asked, "So, you didn`t send these, then?"

"No. No I did not." Kellie was clearly irritated. "Who did?"

"I don`t know."

"What do you mean, you don`t know?"

Brad produced the two cards. "See? No identifying information or return address."

Kellie looked at both sides of the cards and nodded. "You`re right." She shook her head. "This is very weird."

"So, you`re not mad at me, then?"

"No, Brad, I`m not mad at you. But I am worried about who is sending these packages, and what that person`s intentions are."

"Maybe it`s the guys at work, playing a prank on me. They can be such jokers sometimes!"

"Maybe," Kellie said, though she was far from convinced.

Brad read the concern on Kellie`s face and kissed her forehead. "Listen, I`ll just tell the guys that the joke isn`t funny anymore and has to stop. I`m sure they`ll understand."

"What if it`s not them?" Kellie asked.

Brad thought for a moment and replied, "I don`t know."

He suddenly wished he could find a better answer for what was quickly becoming a most unusual situation.

******

The packages kept coming.

One on the Wednesday of each week, just like the first two.

A box of chocolates on the third week. A charm bracelet the next.

Brad had no idea what was in the fifth package. Kellie got home before he did that day, and when he returned he found her visibly shaking and upset. In a flash of anger, Kellie flung the box to the ground, and Brad heard the contents smash into pieces. After trying to calm her down Brad picked the card off the now damaged package and found it addressed exactly the same as all the others.

If he didn`t know before, he certainly knew now that this foolishness had to stop. He promised Kellie that he would call the courier company and instruct them not to deliver anything that did not at least have a return address, and that they would not accept anything unless they signed for it first. She apologized for losing her temper and agreed with this course of action, and they expressed hope that it would work.

Brad made the phone call the next day and was assured by the person from the courier company that they would comply with the request. When nothing else was delivered for two weeks in a row, both Kellie and Brad sighed in relief. They accepted that they may never know who sent these items and why, but it seemed that this mystery was over.

Except it wasn`t.

The following Wednesday, a rainy October day, Brad found another package waiting for him in his locker room at the curling club. He let out an exasperated sigh and picked it up. He examined the card, which was addressed the same as the others, with one major difference; it was written in ink instead of typed out, and the writing was a flowery script, almost certainly a woman`s handwriting. Not Kellie`s though; Brad recognized her handwriting and knew this wasn`t it.

Brad walked over to the office of Russ, his boss, and placed the package on his desk. Russ arched an eyebrow and asked, "What`s this?"

"I was hoping you could tell me," replied Brad.

Russ shook his head. "Did you open it?"

"No."

"Then how should I know?" Russ read the card and chuckled. "And this sure as hell ain`t my handwriting!"

Brad sighed. "I know that. I guess I was, maybe, hoping you saw or knew who delivered this."

"Nope. Sorry Brad."

Brad nodded and frowned. Russ noticed this and decided to dig a little further. "Something on your mind?"

Brad thought for a moment and then sat down in the chair across from Russ`s desk. "The last several weeks, Kellie and I have had a lot of similar packages delivered to our house. All addressed to me, with no return address. We figured out how to stop it a couple weeks ago so I thought whoever was playing this joke on us was done." He tapped the package on the desk and continued, "Until today, that is."

Russ stroked his chin, deep in thought. He asked, "You sure Kellie`s not playing secret admirer?"

Brad smirked, thinking of Kellie destroying the package delivered on the fifth week, and replied, "Believe me Russ, I know for an absolute fact Kellie has nothing to do with this."

"I see. Have you asked anyone here if they did it?"

"Everyone I could think of. No one has fessed up yet."

"Well if I get a chance, I`ll ask around, but I wouldn`t hold my breath."

Brad shook Russ`s hand and thanked him for trying. He took the package with him and stuffed it in his locker, not wanting to open it. The rest of his day passed by without incident, other than word getting around about his latest delivery and him taking some good-natured ribbing over it.

Another package awaited him the next week. He stuffed it in his locker and slammed it shut. Brad hated to admit it, but this whole scenario was bothering him, upsetting his usually calm demeanour.

That night, both Kellie and Brad were tense and on edge. Both hardly said a word to each other, and when they did talk it was in clipped, sometimes harsh one-word sentences. They were both feeling guilty about speaking to each other so unkindly, which made them feel even worse, except they were so riled up they were too proud to call a truce to their hostilities.

They both went to bed still angry. Kellie turned off the lamp and lay on her side. After a couple minutes, she flicked the light back on.

"Brad?"

He sighed. "Yes Kellie?"

"Look, this is ridiculous. We`re both angry and taking it out on each other for no good reason. I`m sorry for being so upset with you."

"No Kellie, I`m the one who should be sorry. I was very harsh with you tonight, and that was wrong of me. Can you forgive me?"

Kellie kissed Brad lovingly on the cheek. "Of course, honey. I`ll forgive you if you forgive me."

"Deal."

"Why don`t we talk about it? It might help us deal with what`s bothering us."

Brad hesitated. "I wish I didn`t have to tell you what happened to me though, because I`m sure it will upset you."

"You know what we talked about Brad. No secrets, right?"

Brad looked at Kellie and sighed again. Finally he said, "OK, well... over the last couple weeks, I have received two more mystery packages at work. Including one today."

Kellie`s face fell. "Damnit!" she cursed. Brad hated to hear that because Kellie didn`t swear often, and when she did she was almost certainly angry or upset.

"What was in those packages, Brad? Tell me!" Kellie demanded.

"I don`t know. I shoved them both in my locker and didn`t open them."

Kellie looked Brad in the eyes and knew instantly he was telling the truth. "Were they addressed the same?"

"Yes, with one exception."

"What`s that?"

"Instead of typing it out, the person who sent it handwrote the address on the card."

It was Kellie`s turn to sigh. "No other identifying marks?"

"None."

"And no one at work is doing this?"

"No one has admitted to it, anyway."

"Damnit!" Kellie swore again.

Brad winced, but continued. "And I`m not sure I can tell the courier to stop sending packages to the club, because we do get them often enough, and we need to for good business reasons. I really don`t know what to do, Kellie. I`ve thought of everything, but I`m at a loss here."

Kellie nodded. "I know you`re doing your best, honey. It`s just a stupid prank."

Brad caressed Kellie`s cheek. "Never mind that for now. Why don`t you tell me about your problems, baby?"

Kellie`s face scrunched up in disgust. "You would not believe who I saw at the gym tonight!"

"Who?"

"Anita Morriss!"

"Anita?" asked Brad in surprise. "Doesn`t she live in the big city?"

"Yes, she does."

"So why would she be here?"

"I don`t know and I didn`t ask."

"Did you talk to her?"

Kellie shook her head. "No, we didn`t talk to each other at all. I saw her across the room, she recognized me, and we just stared holes through each other."

Brad whistled a little. "Well, I know you don`t like her..."

"No, Brad, I HATE her!"

"OK, OK. I know it`s easy for me to say, but you shouldn`t let her get you upset. Remember, you have the upper hand on her now, right?"

Kellie nodded, fondly remembering her emphatic win in provincials last year.

Brad continued, "And who knows, maybe she`s just here for a day or two visiting someone or on some business, and then she`ll be gone and you won`t have to worry about her again until the Canadian finals next year. If she gets there, that is."

"Thanks Brad, you know just what to say to make me feel better."

"I love you, Kellie Ferguson."

"And I love you, Bradley Galenchuk."

They kissed each other good night, chastely at first but it soon became a full make-out session. Before long they were frantically removing their clothing and fondling each other. Brad kissed Kellie`s neck all over and nibbled on her earlobe, making her pleasurably sigh and lean her head back to offer up more of herself to him. His hands cupped and squeezed her firm ass, and then he let one feel up her slit, which he already found to be dripping wet.

"Feel how ready I am for you, baby?" Kellie teased.

"Oh yes sweetie, I want you so bad!" replied Brad.

From there Kellie took the lead, mounting Brad as he was on his back. She kissed and massaged his strong chest and abs. Her delicate hand found and held his strong erect penis; she stroked it sensually a few times, eliciting a satisfied groan from Brad. Kellie shifted to line up his stiff rod with her willing sex and guided it in. She soon engulfed it completely.

"Yes!" they both cried out when she hit bottom.

Kellie started moving slowly up and down but before long was bouncing enthusiastically. She relished the feeling of his hardness and the friction created as it rubbed against her inner walls. Over and over his member slid briefly out of her before filling her back up. His hands again traveled to her sexy butt. Their eyes locked and they smiled at each other as their breathing became more erratic and a sheen of sweat formed on their bodies from their combined exertions. He watched, mesmerized, as she closed her eyes, bit her lower lip and moaned happily while her breasts jiggled with the rhythm of their lovemaking. As he heard her scream and watched her body writhe in orgasm, he felt his shaft tingle, signalling his own impending release.

He had only one conscious thought as his thick semen flowed inside her: make-up sex was really freaking good.

******

The good feelings lasted about a week.

Brad woke the next morning refreshed and energized after having sex with Kellie followed by a restful sleep. He whistled on his way to work, and his mood improved further when he reached his locker and found no new deliveries had been sent his way.

He looked forward to another interesting, busy day at work. The renovations at the curling club were a long, drawn-out process but the results were really starting to be evident. A new refrigeration plant would provide better and more consistent ice. The locker rooms were expanded and furnished with better amenities. More spectator seats were added. The building as a whole was modernized and upgraded. Brad was proud of the hard work he and his colleagues put in to bring this project to fruition, and he was also proud of Kellie, for it was her talent, personality and compelling story that brought publicity and, more importantly, helped bring money for the project to be undertaken in the first place.

It wasn`t until the beginning of the following week when Brad noticed the envelope taped to the door of his locker. He sighed heavily when he saw it as it was ruining his perfectly good mood. He ripped the envelope off the door and studied it. The handwriting appeared the same as the last two packages delivered to him at the curling club. Only, this envelope was addressed, "To My Secret Crush".

Brad stared at the envelope, wide-eyed, not fully believing what he read. He took a quick look around to ensure no one was there, and then sat down on the bench. He considered just tearing the envelope into many pieces, but he also couldn't deny the growing sense of curiosity, wondering just what was inside. He spent a few agonizing minutes debating the two choices, changing his mind about a hundred times in the process.

In the end, curiosity won out. He carefully opened the envelope and found a one-page letter, written in the same immaculate handwriting. He read the contents of the letter...

Brad,

You don't know me yet, but I have been admiring you from afar for some time now. You are the sexiest man I have ever laid eyes on. I long to run my fingers over your powerful, muscled body, and I crave the sensation of your strong hands lovingly touching and dominating me. My pussy tingles at the mere thought of your hard cock filling me like no man ever has.

I hope you liked the gifts I`ve sent you these past weeks. They are small tokens of appreciation, but rest assured that I can give you more... so much more. More than you`ve ever dreamed of.

Soon, when the time is right, I will make myself known to you, and believe me, the wait will be worth it. For now, imagine the hottest woman you can think of offering her body to you, and know that all your dreams will cum true!

From, your Sexy Secret Admirer

Brad read the letter again, and then a third time. The words on the page dripped with wanton sexuality, and the brazen nature of the whole enterprise, starting right from the delivery of that damned little bonsai tree, really stuck with him. If the author of this letter really was the same person who had sent him all these other gifts, then it hinted at a knowledge she had of him that he found deeply unsettling.

Yet even with all that said, Brad also admitted to himself, somewhat ashamedly, that he was intrigued. The fact that another woman apparently found him sexy was, if he were completely honest with himself, quite an ego booster. He would never pursue this other avenue, however; he could not and would not ever cheat on Kellie, of that he was certain. Kellie was his soul mate and he loved her with every fibre of his being, so why would he ever throw that away? Still, there was no denying that he took some pleasure in knowing he had that same kind of effect on another woman.

All these thoughts, the unease, the intrigue and the guilt and shame that came with it, waged war in his head. The only thing he knew for sure right now is that Kellie would never know of the existence of this letter. Despite her recent reminder of their "no-secrets" pact, Brad decided there were some things she was simply better off not knowing. He crumpled the paper into a ball and casually tossed it in the waste basket.

As Brad left the locker room to begin his day's tasks, Russ caught his attention and asked him to join him in his office. When Brad did so he saw that sitting next to Russ was an attractive young woman. Brad thought he vaguely recognized her but couldn't quite put a finger on it.

"Brad," Russ said, "I'd like to introduce you to Anita Morriss."

Anita extended a small hand. "Hello Brad. It's a pleasure to meet you."

Brad was startled but tried to recover his composure as quickly as possible. He tried to be as professional as possible in the circumstances. "Welcome, Anita," he answered, shaking her hand. "What brings you around these parts?"

"I've heard that your facility had some renovations done, and I must say from what I've seen so far it looks great! I also thought it would be good for my team to break away from the usual routine and go for some old-fashioned team-building."

"How long do you plan on staying?" Brad asked.

Russ answered for her. "She and her team have decided to visit our humble town and practice here for a few weeks. Anita decided to get here a day or two early. The rest of the team will be here on Monday and they will stay until mid-December so they can go back to the big city and enjoy Christmas with their families and all that good stuff. I`d like you to show Anita and her team our new facilities and make sure they are properly looked after while they are here. "

Brad nodded, but all he could think of was what Kellie`s reaction would be when she learned of this turn of events. He did not like where this was going. At all.

He spoke up. "Anita, I have to apologize, but I do have some other work-related issues I need to discuss with Russ in private."

"Oh, I understand, no problem at all Brad. I`ll just wait outside and when you two are finished we can talk about the rest of the preparations," Anita replied, smiling sweetly. She stepped outside and closed the office door behind her.

Brad started in on his boss immediately. "Holy crap, Russ, you`re killing me here. Do you have any idea..."

Russ held up a hand to interrupt. "Say no more, Brad. I know I`m putting you in a difficult position. I know Kellie won`t be happy to hear about this."

Brad scoffed. "That`s putting it mildly. She`ll freak out, trust me."

Russ continued, "Brad, you have to understand where I`m coming from. The board of directors have told me in no uncertain terms that we have to treat Anita`s visit with the utmost importance. They clearly told me that I had to put my best man on it. That`s why I chose you for the job. I hope you take it as a compliment, even if it puts you in a bind on the home front."

Brad sighed and shook his head. "OK, Russ, I`ll do it, only because you asked me to. But don`t be surprised if Kellie doesn`t send you a Christmas card this year."

"I'll take my chances," Russ said. He then summoned Anita back into the office and they planned more of the logistics of her team's visit and training time.

Later that evening Brad returned home to a very agitated Kellie. "Brad, I'm glad you're home!" she exclaimed. "I've been hearing rumours all day that Anita will be staying in town for a few more weeks! Please tell me it's not true!"

Brad's face fell. "Sorry Kellie, I have bad news. I have first-hand knowledge that those rumours are indeed true."

"What? What do you mean?"

"I was formally introduced to her at work today. Apparently Anita decided to train with her team in town here for a few weeks to help test the club's new facilities, for team bonding and stuff like that." Brad sighed. "Russ asked me to help take care of her team while they are here, help arrange their practice schedules and show them around, stuff like that."

Kellie drew her face up into a grimace, and balled up her fists. "Unbelievable!" she yelled. "That... that bitch! She has no place coming here!" She looked thoroughly miserable and nearly vibrated with rage.

"Shh, Kellie, it`s OK," Brad tried to soothe Kellie with his words and his touch, gently holding her and softly running his hand through her hair.

When he thought she had calmed down somewhat, he spoke again.

"Kellie? Can I ask you a question?"

Kellie did not say anything, only nodding for Brad to continue.

"Why does Anita upset you so much? I mean, I know she defeated you quite a few times before last year, and that probably wasn`t fun, but this seems to be so much on a personal level. I don`t get it."

Kellie looked down for a while before making eye contact with Brad. She said, "I guess I never did tell you the whole story, did I?"

Brad thought for a moment before shaking his head no.

"Well," Kellie said, "Anita constantly insulted and threatened me before our matches. She called me every insult she could think of, and she tried to turn the rest of my team against me a few times. She said very cruel and hurtful things, ridiculing me for my difficult family life, and... just so many other things that I can`t even bring myself to say, they hurt so much. I thought maybe I was over it, but seeing her in town the last few days and hearing she`ll be here for some time, it`s just bringing the bad memories, the pain, all of it back. And I hate it, Brad! I hate her, and I hate how that makes me feel!"

Kellie was sobbing now, and it killed Brad a little inside to see her like this. He held her and tried again to soothe her. She nuzzled into his shoulder, looking for support and comfort.

"Honey," Brad said, "everything will be OK. I`ll find out on Monday what their practice schedule is and I`ll tell you so you can arrange your team`s practice times around that. You won`t have to see her at all while she`s here. And yes I`ll have to work with her, but it`s just my job, strictly business. Kellie, we`ll get through this, before you know it she`ll be gone and this will be all over."

He kissed the top of her head and she snuggled even deeper into his strong arms. He lightly ran one hand through her hair and the other down her left shoulder and arm. Before long he heard her breathing slow into a rhythmic pattern. He looked closer at her and, sure enough, she had fallen asleep.

Brad carried Kellie into their bed, being careful not to wake her. He watched her beautiful face as she slept, still holding him tightly in a loving embrace. He kept watching her until he could keep his eyes open no longer, falling into his own deep slumber.

******

She was one demanding guest.

Brad found himself being ran ragged during Anita`s visit. She was a perfectionist and demanded nothing less than perfection from those around her. She wanted to learn about and use all the new facilities, she required different ice conditions so her team could practice different ways, and she wanted the biggest and best of everything and would not take no for an answer. She was seemingly doing her best not to be nasty and overbearing, however, and her presence had the full support of club management so it was hard for Brad to say no. All in all, it made for a lot of long days.

About two weeks in, there was another envelope taped to Brad`s locker. He opened it to find a letter and another envelope, plainly marked and filled with what felt like some moderately heavy papers. After ensuring the coast was clear, he read the letter.

My sexy, sexy Brad.

Each day that passes is agonizingly long and slow without you, yet it brings me one day closer to being in your strong arms. I walk around constantly horny, dreaming of you ravishing my hot little body over and over, me screaming your name in ecstasy as you fuck me and mark me as yours.

I hope these pictures tide you over until I give myself to you as the real thing. Look at them as you imagine plunging your hard cock into my wet pussy and making both our dreams cum true.

Your SEXY Secret Admirer.

"Pictures?" Brad said out loud. Was this really happening? Despite his better judgement, he opened the second envelope.

There were six photos in total, all in black and white, all of a nude woman. Tasteful nudes, yet nudes all the same. The expert use of shadowing and cropping meant that the woman`s face and thus true identity was hidden, but little else was left to the imagination. The woman`s body was lean and strong, yet very feminine. A pair of perky breasts with small button-like nipples sat on top of a tight and finely curved torso. Her legs looked long and finely sculpted, and the pictures taken from the rear displayed a firm young ass and just a hint of the treasure between her legs.

Brad found himself getting aroused. This woman wasn`t Kellie; the body lacked certain defining characteristics of hers that he had known very intimately. And he was pretty sure he would have known if she had gone to a studio and had pictures like these taken of her.

But damn if this woman wasn`t sexy in her own right. She had a similar body type to Kellie, the same type he naturally preferred in women. Lithe and athletic. Curvy in just the right places. Her ass looked particularly scrumptious...

Brad put the pictures down and rubbed his temples, trying to clear his mind. He knew it was wrong to feel this way about another woman. Everything about this was wrong. For a man who usually felt in command of the situations around him, the total lack of control he had over this game this mystery woman was playing with him was the most infuriating thing of all.

Just as Brad was doing a slow burn, Anita poked her head in. "Hi Brad!" she said.

"Huh?!" Brad sat up with a jump. "Oh, Anita, hi. Sorry, you just startled me a bit."

"Sorry about that," she giggled. "Hey, what are you looking at there?"

"What? Oh, it`s nothing," Brad said as casually as he could. He tossed the pictures into his locker and shut it with a bang.

Anita just shrugged and sat down next to Brad. He could detect a faint smell of baby powder and her fruity shampoo. "So what`s on the agenda today?" he asked.

"I`ve decided to give the girls a day off. I`ve worked them pretty hard so far and they could use a little break. Frankly so could I." At this Anita did a full-body stretch, appearing to put her otherwise fully-clothed body on full display. Brad was too polite to stare, but he did cast a sideways glance at Anita while at the same time admonishing himself for doing so.

Anita placed a delicate hand on Brad`s arm as she spoke again. "I just wanted to thank you Brad for your hospitality so far. I know I`ve been pretty demanding and I`ve asked a lot of you, but you`ve done really great work so far."

"Thanks. Just doing my job," replied Brad.

"I still appreciate it though. So does the rest of my team."

"Don`t mention it."

Anita paused and then chuckled a little, saying, "I probably shouldn`t say this without them knowing... but the rest of the girls think you`re pretty cute, Brad!"

Brad blushed and stammered, "Um... well, I... uh..."

Anita then whispered conspiratorially, "You know, I have to agree with them. You`re pretty hot stuff."

"Well, I`m flattered, really," Brad said, recovering his composure and showing the engagement ring on his hand. "But as you can see, I`m already spoken for."

Anita nodded. "You and Kellie, huh?"

"Yeah," Brad answered, looking at Anita warily. "How did you know? I don`t remember mentioning her to you. Did I?"

There was silence for a long time, but it looked to Brad that Anita really wanted to speak her mind. Instead she exhaled and shook her head, eventually saying, "You know what, that`s not really any of my business. I think I`m going to go for a coffee. Thanks again Brad, see you soon."

And with that she was gone. Brad sat still, staring at nothing in particular for several minutes, trying to wrap his head around the conversation. He suddenly wished Anita and her team`s visit would be cut short so his and Kellie`s lives could return to some level of normalcy.

******

This was not what he needed right now.

Anita continued to be insistent on having things done perfectly, her way. That combined with his regular work duties made for long days for Brad. This meant less time for him to spend with Kellie, which made her even more on edge, which, considering her archenemy was in town for so long and how she found that so unnerving, was pretty seriously on edge.

Furthermore, Anita had been making other odd little comments to Brad whenever she had a chance. Dropping hints about the lack of available bachelors in town, and about how much she missed the men in her city neighbourhood. Subtle remarks that hinted at a possible attraction she had for him. Worst of all, she made a few comments that, while perhaps not outright insulting to Kellie, could leave the impression that she thought he could do much better than her. She timed these comments perfectly and never gave him an opportunity to respond.

And now, at the end of another gruelling day, physically and mentally, there was another envelope taped to his locker door.

Another goddamned envelope.

He tore it off the locker and ripped it open, nearly shredding the letter inside in the process.

Whenever Brad looked back on this chapter in his life, he wondered what would have happened had he just destroyed the letter. Instead, with his heart pounding inside his chest, he read it.

Brad,

The time for playing games is over now. I must have you! This game of seduction has been very pleasing and thrilling for me, but I cannot bear the thought of another day without you. My pussy is on fire, begging for your touch.

I know you are with a woman now, but I also know I can take care of your needs so much better than her. Oh yes, Brad, you may not know my true identity just yet but I know so much about you. And I`ve been much closer to you than you could imagine. I`ve seen the look in your eyes, I know how much you want me, and it only fuels my desire for you.

Don`t deny yourself this ultimate pleasure. Don`t deny me. You know you want this. Let me make your dreams cum true.

Your Secret Admirer

P.S. Look up.

Confused, Brad did indeed look up. His breath caught in his throat.

"Anita," he gasped.

Anita Morriss stood at the entrance, wearing a long trench coat and black high heels. She had a small, seductive smile on her face. Then, with a dramatic flair, she pulled her coat open and let it fall to the floor in a pool around her legs. She was now covered in only a black lacy bra and matching panties that left little to the imagination. She strutted forward towards Brad, who was by now transfixed by the beautiful woman before him; the letter he had read moments earlier had since fluttered softly to the floor. She walked slowly in a circle around him, letting the fingers of one hand trail through his hair. The seductive smile had not left her lips, and she was making a satisfied noise that seemed to be a hybrid of purring and a deeper feline growl.

"Anita, what are you doing?" Brad asked.

She gave him a throaty chuckle. "Isn`t it obvious?"

Not waiting for him to answer, she sat in his lap, straddling him. He could feel his hard-on grow as she rubbed her panty-covered mound on his crotch and ran her hands over his chest.

He gulped and closed his eyes. Suddenly, he understood everything. He was upset at himself for taking so long to clue in, but then again she had laid out her plan so methodically. It was brilliant in a devious way, he supposed.

"You," he finally said as he opened his eyes. "It was you all along, wasn`t it? Sending those packages and leaving these letters for me to read. You did all this."

Anita giggled, bit her bottom lip and nodded her head. "I was wondering if you would ever figure it out before now. In a way I`m glad you didn`t though. Like I wrote, this chase has been a big thrill for me. And now, I have my ultimate prize."

She teasingly licked his cheek and his ear, causing Brad to sigh in pleasure. "So I`m just the goal of your fun little game, am I? Just prey you were seeking to capture?" he asked, his will power diminishing by the second from Anita`s expert seduction.

"Mmmm, you know you can be more than that, big boy," Anita whispered in his ear. "You can be my strong man, my knight in shining armour, and I can be the kind of woman you need, the kind of woman Kellie could only dream of being."

Kellie.

The sound of her name quickly jolted Brad back to reality. He gently yet firmly lifted Anita off his lap and sat her down on the bench. He was quickly up on his feet, pacing and nervously laughing. "Whoa, that was a close one," he said, more to himself than to Anita.

He then said to Anita, "Please listen carefully. I mean no disrespect, and I apologize if I have led you on in some way, though I really don`t think I have. In any case I have very nearly made the biggest mistake of my life. I love Kellie with all my heart, and I can`t risk throwing it all away for anything or anyone. You need to get dressed and stop trying to seduce me."

Anita was frustrated but she hid it as best as she could, trying to turn on the charm again. "But Brad, don`t you find me pretty?" she asked, playfully batting her eyelashes.

"You`re a beautiful woman, Anita. I`m sure you can have any other man you choose. Just not me. These games have to stop."

Her voice was edgy, aggressive. "I don`t think you understand, Brad. I`m the kind of woman who gets what she wants." She stopped herself before she came off as too angry and tried a different tack. She smiled and asked, "What would it take to convince you? Because I would do anything to have you as my lover. Anything at all." She took Brad`s hands and placed one on her left breast, the other on her sex. She humped his hand slowly, back and forth, back and forth, feeling the wetness spread within her. She stared into his deep blue eyes, practically daring him to refuse her offer.

Brad could feel Anita's arousal, both her diamond-hard nipple and her quickly moistening pussy, through the thin lace of her lingerie. He swallowed and inhaled deeply as his cock twitched and hardened again. It would be so easy to give in to temptation, to indulge his carnal desires and fuck this beautiful woman who was basically throwing herself at his feet.

No. I must resist, he thought to himself. He removed his hands from her body and took two deliberate steps backwards. "I told you, I love Kellie. She's the only woman for me, now and forever. There's nothing you can do to get me to cheat on her."

He watched Anita begin to fume, her face growing redder by the second. It wasn't an attractive look for her, Brad thought. He was starting to see why Kellie held Anita with such disdain.

But then her lips curled into the most devilish smile he had ever seen on anyone in his life. He was completely unsure how to react. Before he could ask her what she was so damn happy about, Anita embraced Brad and kissed him with as much hunger and passion as she could gather. He tried to break the kiss but she would have none of that. She took the lead again, holding on to him tightly and surprising him with her strength. She planted his hands on her ass and kissed him hard again, her tongue parting her lips and seeking entry into his. He barely responded to the kiss, but he didn`t break it either despite the voice in his head screaming at him to do so. His mind was a swirling mass of confusion and bewilderment.

Anita broke the kiss and looked into Brad`s eyes, still sporting the same grin from before, even breaking out into an evil little laugh. He was preparing to ask her just what the hell was going on.

Then he heard a very familiar voice from behind him.

"Brad?"

His eyes grew wide in shock and fear. He slowly turned around to see Kellie. Her lower lip was quivering and tears were rolling down her face.

"Why, Brad? Why?" she asked.

He was dumbstruck. He tried to speak, his mouth made speaking-like motions, but no words came out.

"Answer me, damnit!" Kellie yelled.

Finally he stammered, "Kellie, please... this isn`t what it looks like... I can explain..." He cringed at his own words, hating how weak and goddamned clichéd they sounded.

"Shut up, Brad! Just shut up! God damn you, you bastard! I never want to see you again!!" Kellie ran out of the room, sobbing all the way.

Brad ran into the hallway. "No, please Kellie, come back! Don`t go!" It was too late. Kellie was gone.

He walked in a daze back into the locker room and slumped on to the bench. He then felt Anita`s hands trailing over him again and heard her say in a seductive voice, "Well, looks like we`ll have time to play after all."

He didn`t feel arousal this time. Only burning, white hot fury.

"Get out," he said in a dead flat tone.

"Oh, I think we both know you don`t really want me to..."

"I SAID GET OUT!!" In a flash Brad stood up and whirled around, adrenaline coursing through his veins. He saw Anita put her hands in front of her in a defensive stance, and as he wondered why he realized his right fist was cocked back, ready to strike. This made him even angrier, and without thinking he turned and drove his fist into a metal locker with all his might, connecting partly with the door but more with the hard, unyielding frame surrounding it.

The pain was blinding, searing. He howled in agony. He didn`t even notice Anita pick up her coat and run away as fast as she could.

The anger drained from Brad, and all that was left was the pain of his mangled hand, which was nothing compared to the pain of his broken heart. He collapsed to the floor and wept bitterly.

******

He found him there about an hour later.

Russ had just finished meeting with Anita and her team. Anita had announced they were cutting their visit short immediately, two weeks early. Russ was concerned that this would reflect badly on the club as a whole, and more specifically his job performance. She assured him that they had no problem with the club or its employees and enjoyed their stay, but otherwise she was very vague about their reasons for leaving. After they left Russ decided he needed to find Brad to see if he could shed some light on the situation.

After a few minutes of searching Russ found Brad in the employees locker room. He was stunned at what he saw. There was a massive dent in one of the lockers. Brad was slumped on the floor and looked to be in a wretched state. One of his hands was bloody, broken and swollen to twice its normal size.

Russ managed to get Brad up and immediately drove him to the local hospital. En route, he asked, "Brad, what happened?"

Silence.

"Anita just told me her team had decided to leave now. Do you know anything about this?"

More silence.

"Brad, I really wish you would..."

"I don`t want to talk about it right now, Russ."

Russ suddenly felt very uncomfortable and decided to stop his inquiries for now. He drove the rest of the way to the hospital without saying another word.

After being told Brad would have to wait overnight to have an X-ray and surgery scheduled Russ went home for the night. He got a phone call the next night from the hospital`s head nurse who told him Brad`s surgery was done and he was being released, and since he helped admit him to the hospital would he please pick him up as well. Russ was even more curious now but he knew something had to have gone badly wrong if he instead of Kellie had to get Brad.

He found Brad in the waiting area, a large cast on his hand but otherwise looking just as miserable as before. Russ was about to speak but Brad interrupted him.

"Russ, I apologize for being rude to you yesterday, but in my defense, it was the worst day of my life. I promise I`ll tell you all I can but not right now. It hurts too much. Also, if I could crash at your place for a while I would appreciate that. I have nowhere else to go."

"What about Kellie, Brad?"

Brad just shook his head. "I can`t go back there," was all he could say.

It hurt Russ to see his friend so depressed so he agreed to let him use his guest bedroom until things got sorted out. He also allowed him to use a short-term medical leave from work as he would not be able to do much with a broken hand.

Brad barely spoke two words over the next couple days. That second evening, Russ, out of great concern, said, "Brad, I don`t want to force you, but it might help at least a little to talk about what happened."

Brad looked totally defeated. He sighed heavily and finally decided to tell his long-time boss and friend what happened. "Anita tried to seduce me."

Russ nodded. He had some suspicions, and this just confirmed that at least one of them were true. He tried to keep an open mind and not judge his friend until he finished the story.

Brad continued. "Remember all those packages and letters? She sent them all. It was part of her whole plan or game or... whatever. She finally revealed everything to me... almost literally... that night. I guess it was that same night she later told you they were leaving early. Anyway, the really scary part is it almost worked. Anita looked so hot and was pushing all my buttons, I damn near fucked her right then and there. But I resisted because I wouldn`t be able to live with myself if I cheated on Kellie. Kellie`s the best thing that ever happened in my life... you know that Russ, don`t you?"

Russ nodded again.

"And you believe me, right? You believe that I`m telling the truth when I say I didn`t cheat on Kellie, right?"

"Yes, Brad, I do believe you, absolutely."

"Thanks Russ. Anyway, all of a sudden Anita just kisses and gropes me out of the blue. I`m so shocked I don`t react. I just stand there like an idiot letting her do whatever the hell she wanted. It just happened that at that very moment, Kellie walked in." Brad started to sob and choke at this point. "She thought I was kissing Anita for real. Then Kellie... she... told me she... never wanted to see me again."

Wow, Russ thought as Brad bowed his head and sobbed harder. This was bad. Real bad. He took a couple of deep breaths before speaking. "Brad,

I`m here for you. I`ll help you any way that I can." He didn`t know what else to say.

Brad looked up and nodded. He appreciated the support from Russ. But unless something drastic happened, he figured it was going to be a long time before he would recover from these deep emotional scars. If he ever would.

******

She was despondent.

Kellie missed having Brad around. Even with everything that had happened, she genuinely missed having him at her side. They had been through so much and did everything together. She felt his absence most keenly at night, when she was in bed; there was now open space where he had usually slept peacefully. She missed feeling his body heat keeping her warm under the covers. And, if she was being completely honest with herself, she missed the sex, too.

But every time she thought briefly about asking him to come back, and every time she saw his cell number or Russ`s number on the caller ID screen of her phone, her mind turned back to the sight of him making out with a half-naked Anita, and she became angry all over again. Bad enough that he could so casually toss away their relationship for some cheap sex. But with Anita! That witch! Kellie knew she could never forgive Brad for such a betrayal.

In the days afterwards, Kellie`s curling teammates and best friends had called her on the phone every day, asking and even begging her to either visit them or let them visit her, just so she could talk about it and maybe find a way to emerge from her funk. Kellie had successfully rebuffed them every time. She looked and felt a mess, her eyes red from constant crying, and she simply did not feel like moving on at this point.

This continued until a week later, when that evening Kellie heard the doorbell ring at the front door. At first she didn`t move, but whoever was at the door was insistent and would not take the hint. Reluctantly, she got up to answer the door. There stood her three teammates; Jennifer Janik, the vice-skip, Sandra Morgan, the second, and Jennifer`s younger sister Amber, the lead.

"Alright, skip," Sandra said, using their preferred nickname for Kellie," enough moping around and living like a hermit. We`re going to have a girls night in!"

"Oh I don`t know girls, you don`t really want to be around me, I`m not much fun right now," Kellie replied.

"Sorry skip, it`s all decided, we`re not taking no for an answer!" Jennifer said.

Amber excitedly chimed in, "Look! We got snacks and chick flicks! Come on, it will be great!"

Kellie relented and the three young ladies piled in to the house, giggling along the way. All four of them stuffed themselves with popcorn and laughed themselves silly during the movies. For the first time in a long while Kellie forgot about her troubles and had fun with her three best friends in the world. She did notice Jennifer looking at her smart phone and texting throughout, but she didn`t think much of it at the time as Jennifer was always playing with that darned thing.

After the second movie was finished, Jennifer checked her phone again and gave a small nod to Amber and Sandra. There was an awkward pause as the room grew quiet, before Sandra spoke up. "Skip, we need to talk..."

"There`s nothing to talk about," Kellie interrupted, knowing exactly what they were trying to do.

The other three ladies looked at each other, unsure of how to proceed. Jennifer looked at the other two with a nod and a look that said, I`ve got this.

She turned to Kellie and said, "Skip, we know what happened. We know the whole story about you and Brad, and Anita. More than you realize, actually."

Kellie was incredulous. "What?! How?! That`s impossible! I never told you what happened, but even if I did it doesn`t matter. I was there! I saw everything!! There IS no more to the story!! Brad`s a cheating bastard and that`s it!!"

Jennifer knew how furious Kellie was. If the plan she worked out with Amber and Sandra didn`t come off, there was no telling what their future held. They knew they had something special with Kellie, both in the strength and success of their curling exploits, but more importantly in their combined friendship, which had been tested at times but was now truly deep and long-lasting. Now their leader was in need and they had to be there for her. Despite Jennifer`s youth, she had a real self-confident attitude, and she used this belief to do what she and her other teammates knew needed to be done.

"Skip, do you trust us?"

Kellie eyed Jennifer, Sandra and Amber warily as she wondered what they were up to. She sighed and said, "Yes Jen, I trust you, I trust all of you, but..."

That was all Jennifer needed to hear. "Awesome! Just a sec, OK?" She sent another text message, and just a couple of minutes thereafter came a knock on the door. Kellie was confused as Jennifer told her, "It`s OK skip, I`ll get it."

Jennifer went to answer the door and returned with a guest. Kellie recognized her. She was Heather Nelson, the lead player for Anita`s team and a good friend of Jennifer. Kellie never raised any objections to Jennifer being friends with someone from Anita`s team, especially since Jennifer and Heather were friends before Jennifer even met Kellie. But under these circumstances it didn`t feel appropriate for Heather to be here.

"Heather," Kellie said, "I mean no disrespect, but... why are you here? I don`t think it`s right, what we`re talking about is none of your business."

Jennifer opened her mouth to speak but Heather stopped her and spoke instead. "No offense taken, Kellie. Thing is, your teammates, your friends, they asked me to be here. I have something that they, and I, think you need to hear."

She reached into her purse, produced a small Dictaphone and handed it to Jennifer, who turned to her skip and said, "Kellie, what you do and the decisions you make in your personal life are normally none of our business. But this whole situation affects us all, and we think that, before you make any final decisions about you and Brad, you should have all the information possible to help you make the right ones."

Before Kellie could say anything else, Jennifer pressed play on the recording device. Kellie heard what sounded like a conversation between Heather and Anita. She guessed Heather had recorded it without Anita`s knowledge or consent. She listened closely once the initial small talk had finished.

Heather: "So what`s really going on, Anita? Why are we leaving tomorrow?"

Anita: "Ugh, haven`t you had enough of this shitty one-horse town?"

Heather: "Well, I do miss being home... but that doesn`t answer my question."

Anita: "Alright, if you must know. I had other reasons for coming here besides team building."

Heather: "Why am I not surprised? It wouldn`t have had anything to do with the guy from the curling club helping us out, would it?"

Anita: "Maybe. He`s pretty fucking sexy, isn`t he?"

Heather: "Well, yes he is, but Brad`s engaged. Jennifer told me about him and Kellie a while ago, and besides, that ring on his finger is a dead giveaway."

Anita: "Heather, you know I don`t allow fraternizing with the enemy..."

Heather: "Jeez, Anita, we`ve talked about this..."

Anita: "Besides, girl, you honestly think I didn`t notice the ring?"

(Pause)

Heather: "OK, if you knew that, then what were you trying to pull?"

Anita: "Trying to fuck the shit out of Brad! Duh!"

Heather: "Even though he`s engaged?"

Anita: (sighing) "What are you, a prude? Besides, who do you think a red-blooded male would really prefer? That nerd Kellie, or me?"

Heather: "Well, in case you noticed, I`m not a guy, so..."

Anita: "OK, whatever. Anyway, I had the whole thing planned. I sent a bunch of gifts to their house and then to the club. Once we were there I left him some secret admirer letters, and in one I included some of those nude pictures I had done..."

Heather: "That`s cold."

Anita: "... then finally I figured he`d be begging for me. I saw him in the employee locker room and got down to my bra and panties. He looked so fucking hot and delicious, I wanted to do him right there and then. I was putting all my best moves on him. But he didn`t take the bait! Can you believe that?"

Heather: "Hmmm, well you do usually get any man you go after, `cause you are kind of a..."

Anita: "Shut up, I know! But he was all like I can`t cheat on Kellie, she`s the only woman for me, I love her so much... puh-leeze! He must be just as big a nerd as she is!"

Heather: "So just because you struck out, we`re leaving?"

Anita: "No, just shut up for a second, damnit, and listen! It actually worked out in the end, I couldn`t believe my luck! Just as I was about to leave and try again another day, Kellie comes walking in! So I kiss Brad and he`s just stunned! Doesn`t move a muscle. It was kind of like kissing a wax dummy, actually, since he didn`t do anything back, but let me tell you, the look on Kellie`s face was priceless!"

Heather: "And what does that accomplish, exactly?"

Anita: "Oh come on Heather, do I have to spell it out for you? Even if Kellie just thinks Brad cheated on her, she`ll dump him and be a complete mess! Then our biggest competition will be out of the way and we`ll win the national championship again, hands down! Don`t forget the big picture here, that`s what it`s all about."

Heather: "Uh... yeah. Yeah of course."

Anita: (sighing again) "Too bad in a way, I really wanted to fuck him, he looked like he had a big cock and I haven`t been properly laid in a good couple months. But I achieved the main goal here. You`ll thank me later. I tell you, Kellie will be such a wreck she might never throw a rock properly again. Then everyone will know last year was a fluke and that I`m the best curler in the world and we`re the real team to beat!"

The rest of the conversation was inconsequential. After a few seconds of static Jennifer stopped the recording.

Kellie was stunned. She realized what that recorded conversation really meant. Brad was obviously too shocked by everything that happened to properly explain himself that day, but he really had been faithful to her all along. And she told him she never wanted to see him again! Now what? She sat down on her chair, hands over her eyes, and mumbled, "My god, what have I done?"

Heather then spoke. "Kellie, I wouldn`t be so hard on yourself. You got played by a manipulative, vindictive bitch. I`ve seen it happen before, you`re not the first and you probably won`t be the last."

Kellie looked up, smirked and shook her head.

"Besides," said Jennifer, "if the love you and Brad have for each other is as strong as we think it is, you two will get back together, put this whole mess behind you and become even stronger for it."

Kellie nodded as a single tear ran down her cheek. She realized they were right. She knew what she had to do, but there was one question she needed answered first.

"Heather, can I ask you something?"

"Sure."

"What made you decide to do this? I`m just curious. I mean, I`m glad you`re doing it, don`t get me wrong..."

Heather interrupted, "It`s OK, Kellie. Jennifer`s a really, really good friend, and seeing what Anita was doing and how it would affect you and Jennifer and Amber and Sandra, I just couldn`t sit idly by and do nothing. Jennifer would have never forgiven me, and rightly so. Also I guess I`m just tired of Anita`s attitude. I mean, I want to win, for sure, I`m a competitor like you all are, and winning is very important to me. But not like this. Not this way."

"You know, Anita will probably kick you off the team for this."

Heather shrugged. "I`ve kind of come to terms with that. If she does, fine. If she doesn`t... hell, I might just quit anyway. Besides... I`m not sure whether I had a choice in the matter."

"What do you mean, Heather?"

"Well... Jennifer kind of made me tell the rest of you once I told her..."

Kellie looked at Jennifer. "And how did you manage that?"

Jennifer and Heather looked at each other with strange expressions on their faces. Kellie laughed and said "Actually, you know what? Never mind, I don`t need to know."

Jennifer and Heather sighed in relief at the exact same time, which made everyone laugh heartily.

Kellie hugged Heather and each of her teammates in turn. Eventually they all formed a big group hug. Kellie spoke to Heather first. "Thank you so much, Heather. You don`t know how much this means to me. You didn`t have to but you decided to do the right thing and reveal the truth. Because you decided to help me I`ll be able to get my life back in order. You`re obviously a special person, and any friend of Jennifer is a friend of mine."

"Mine too!" Sandra and Amber chimed in. Jennifer just smiled brightly.

Kellie then addressed her teammates directly. "And thank all of you, Sandra, Amber and Jennifer. You`re the best friends a girl could have, I don`t know what I`d do without you."

"Anytime, skip. We love you. We`ll always have your back, right girls?" Jennifer said, and Sandra and Amber enthusiastically agreed.

Kellie checked the time and said, "Thanks again girls, I love you too, all of you. But now I have to kick you girls out!"

Jennifer, Sandra, Amber and Heather all groaned.

Kellie smiled. "Sorry, but it`s getting late, and I`ll need a good night`s sleep so I can be well-rested enough to get my man back tomorrow!"

The women all cheered in delight.

******

It was an unfamiliar feeling for him.

For the first time in his life, Brad wished he could be anywhere on earth but the curling club.

Russ and his other friends at work had been a great source of support, but Brad knew some of them were too young or immature to understand. They had been telling him it was better to be single and play the field, and that he`d find another girl who would want to screw his brains out. But he didn`t want another girl. He wanted his soul mate back. He wanted Kellie. At least Russ, god love him, understood what he was going through. He talked to Brad at length trying to help him and give him any kind of advice he thought might help, and he allowed his friend to stay with him until he got back up on his feet and to take as much time as he needed before returning to work.

But Brad became bored and restless moping around Russ`s house all day. Kellie never answered any of his phone calls, and there was nothing for him to do during the day except watch lousy TV and wallow in his self-pity. He didn`t know if he`d be able to do anything constructive with his busted hand, but he figured anything was better than being enclosed by the four walls of Russ`s guest room.

Coming back to the scene of the "crime", however, felt more and more like a big mistake. He kept replaying the events of that fateful day in his head, over and over, until he was nearly emotionally overwhelmed.

He shook his head as if trying to empty it of its bad memories. He reached to open his locker and fumbled with the lock for a minute before realizing he was using his useless broken hand to do so. He sighed heavily.

Then he heard a very familiar voice from behind him.

"Hi Brad."

He turned around to see her, and his eyes brightened immediately. "Kellie!" he exclaimed, barely able to contain his happiness.

Kellie was about to speak, but first she noticed the cast on his hand and wrist. "Brad, what happened to your hand?" she asked with concern.

Brad`s face went red with embarrassment. "You`ll probably just laugh."

"Brad, I promise I will do no such thing. Tell me. Please."

He looked at her eyes focusing in on him, and knew he could not refuse her request. "After you left, she tried to seduce me again," he said while hanging his head, not wanting to say Anita`s name out loud. "I don`t know, maybe she figured if you thought I was cheating I might as well get my money`s worth. Anyway, I just couldn`t believe she had the nerve to do that after what she just did to me... I mean, to us. It just made me real mad, so I almost drilled her. That made me even more mad, and... I don`t know, I guess I just lost my mind. I punched the hell out of this," he said, pointing to the dented locker, "and broke my hand. Busted it up big-time."

He then looked up and said with a rueful smile, "Pretty smart, huh?"

"Oh, you poor baby!" replied Kellie. She tenderly kissed his hand all over, and it filled his heart with love for her all over again.

A naughty smile then crept over her face. "You know, I kind of wish you did drill her."

"Kellie! That`s not very nice!"

"Come on, Brad, you know you like it."

"I do, it`s kind of hot actually."

They looked at each other for a second and then laughed over their flirty conversation. Brad was filled with hope; it looked like things really would be OK after all. But he wanted to be sure.

"So," he asked, "you`re not mad at me anymore?"

Kellie locked her eyes on him. "No, Brad. I know the whole truth of what happened, and I know you were faithful to me. In fact, I think I need to ask for your forgiveness."

"What? Kellie, you cannot be serious."

"I am, Brad. I jumped to conclusions, and I didn`t trust you. I should have known better, that you would never intentionally do anything to hurt me. I`m sorry."

"Well, I can`t blame you, it must have looked for all the world that I really was going to have sex with her. She tried to break me down, and... oh god Kellie I can`t lie, it almost worked."

"But it didn`t. She tried to seduce you, she`s probably good at it too, she`s pretty on the outside and she always seems to get what she wants. But she didn`t get you. You stayed strong, you resisted and you proclaimed your love for me. You proved to me again how good a man you are and how right I was to give my heart to you."

"I still made a big mistake in how I handled this situation. I wasn`t very smart and I put myself in a bad position. I should have realized what she was doing earlier and stopped it before it got as far as it did. I almost cost us everything. Can you forgive me?"

"Yes, absolutely I forgive you."

"Will you take me back, Kellie? I want to be with you and only you, and I`d do anything to hear you say yes."

"Yes, Brad, please come back to me, I want you more than anything in the world!"

Kellie reached up on her tiptoes to plant a kiss on Brad`s lips. The two hugged each other passionately.

"I love you, Bradley Galenchuk."

"And I love you, Kellie Ferguson."

Kellie snuggled into Brad`s neck, realizing just how much she missed being wrapped up in his strong body and how safe it made her feel. Brad stroked the small of Kellie`s back, recognizing how much he missed the feel of her soft skin and how he could feel her breathing when their bodies were pressed tightly to each other.

Brad asked, "So how did you figure out nothing happened with Anita and me?"

Kellie looked up at Brad and replied, "I won't lie, I had a little help. A lot of help, actually. I'll explain later. Let's just say that getting you to sleep with her was just a secondary goal."

Brad nodded, satisfied for now with waiting for a full explanation, and at the same time knowing exactly what Kellie's last statement meant. "I can't believe she'd stoop so low just to put you off your game."

"I can't believe that little hussy almost got away with it!"

"Well, we're going to make sure she goes oh for three," Brad said as he kissed Kellie on the nose. "Aren't we?"

"What do you mean?"

"Simple. She didn't get me to cheat on you. That's strike one. She didn't break us up and she won't knock you off your game. That's strike two. Strike three is going to be when Amber, Sandra, Jennifer and you prevent her from getting what she wants the most, winning the nationals."

A look of determination was now on Kellie`s face. "Damn right, Brad. Trust me, the girls and I will be ready and we`re going to make sure we do everything possible to win. That witch won`t know what hit her!"

"You go, girls! I`m proud of you, Kellie!"

Kellie nodded. The naughty smile she wore earlier returned.

"There`s something else, Brad," she cooed.

"Oh really? And what`s that?"

Kellie let go of Brad, walked to the door and closed it. She made her way back in front of Brad and sat him down on the bench. She then swayed her hips in a sensual dance, enjoying the surprised yet lustful look on his face. She removed her shirt and gave him an eyeful of her cleavage, enhanced by the push-up lacy bra she was sporting. She then faced away from him and slowly wiggled her jeans over her hips and down her legs, revealing a pair of sexy pink panties. She turned back and looked at him, a low moan escaping her lips as she fondled and shook her ass for her man. Kellie knew how much Brad loved her ass, and she loved teasing him with it, knowing he was staring at her with hungry eyes.

Brad loved the show Kellie was putting on for him, appreciating it even more than usual knowing how close he thought he was to losing her forever. He was by now uncomfortably tight in his jeans, so it was a relief when she undid his belt buckle and pulled his jeans and boxers down and off. His erection bobbed up and down with intent. He knew that somehow in the course of their relationship he helped unleash a wild side in her that neither of them knew existed, and he was about to enjoy some of the fruits of that discovery.

"Brad, I want you to tell me something," Kellie purred in her sultriest voice.

"Yes, Kellie?"

She leaned in closer to him and whispered in his ear. "Someone could walk through that door and catch us at any time. You know that, right?"

He nodded.

"It makes me feel so naughty."

Brad shivered with desire.

"Do you want to help me be naughty, Brad?"

"God, yes!"

Kellie removed her bra and panties, showing off all her womanly treasures. She straddled his lap and teased him some more by grinding on his leg, taking his rock hard member in her hand and stroking it lovingly. He grunted his approval and reached down with his good hand to feel the entrance to her womanhood dripping wet. He deeply inhaled her rich feminine scent, coming from her hot pussy and the wet, sticky spot she was leaving on his thigh.

Brad tried to pick Kellie up but ended up fumbling a bit because of his broken hand. He sighed in frustration, so horny he couldn`t stand it yet part of his body letting him down at the crucial moment.

Kellie stifled a giggle and said, "You poor dear, here, honey, let me help." She raised her hips up and adjusted her body until her slit was lined up with his hard shaft. She sank herself down on it and both lovers groaned with intense pleasure. She rocked up and down slowly at first as they took the time to kiss and hold each other tight. Before long however, their passions inflamed and Kellie quickly bounced on his member as Brad drove up into her on her downward strokes.

Feeling a sudden burst of energy Brad stood up and supported Kellie`s weight with his good hand and his other forearm. She quickly took the hint and wrapped both her arms and her powerful legs around him. From that position Brad thrust into Kellie`s tight entrance with all his strength. She squealed in delight as this new stance was hitting all the right spots.

"Oh yeah Brad, keep doing that, god that feels so good!"

"Kellie my sweet baby, I`m going to cum soon!"

"Yes, me too, honey, please give it to me!"

A few more strokes was all it took before Brad could hold back no longer. His orgasm erupted inside Kellie, hot strands of cum firing deep into her channel. She let out a joyful scream as her own climax shuddered through her beautiful body. They collapsed back down on to the bench, breathing heavily and clinging tightly to each other. Their eyes locked together and they stayed in that position for some time, kissing and silently enjoying the moment they came together as lovers again.

Before long Brad felt himself getting aroused again. Kellie could feel his erection grow and harden until it was poking her stomach.

"Mmmm, is this for me, baby?" she breathed.

"Yes, baby, it`s only for you."

She took his good hand and let him slide a finger into her moist entrance. "Feel how wet I am, baby? It`s all you, always for you."

She cradled his face in her hands as they kissed. He broke the kiss to take one of her breasts in his mouth. He kissed and sucked on it and toyed her nipple gently with his teeth. "Yes!" she hissed and bit her lower lip. She offered him her other breast and he happily obliged, giving it the same treatment as the first.

Kellie was too worked up for a slow session of lovemaking. "Oh god Brad I need you inside me!" she squealed.

Brad was only too happy to oblige. He laid her down on the bench, took hold of his dick with his good hand and aimed it at her wet slit. He sunk inside her depths again and marveled at the heavenly sensations. She locked her legs in a vise-like grip around his torso and plunged him further inside.

"God, Kellie you`re so tight and hot, it feels good, so good!"

"Yes Brad, you fill me up so good! Do me hard! Don`t stop!"

"Oh baby you`re so beautiful!"

"My sexy stud!" Kellie grinned mischievously. "Tell me how nice my ass looks!"

Brad groaned and felt his hard-working cock twitch even more at her words. "Mmmm, Kellie, your ass is the sexiest ever, no woman has an ass like you!" He felt and squeezed her ass with his good hand and pounded into her harder.

She yelped in elation as his loving yet relentless manhood driving deep inside her.

"Oh god I`m going to cum again!" she yelled.

"Yes baby cum for me!"

Kellie`s juices coated his shaft. Her powerful orgasm rocked her body. Brad kept pumping into her as she rode out the aftershocks, until soon wave after wave of his seed shot out of him and flowed inside her.

They were still breathing hard when the door opened.

It was Russ. "Brad, there you are, I..." he started before realizing what was going on. "Oh! Shit!" he said in shock.

Kellie`s mouth opened wide and she clapped her hand to it in surprise. Brad blushed and said, "Uh, hi boss!" Not wanting to let go of Kellie, he reached down to the floor and quickly managed to grab her shirt so she could at least partially cover herself.

"I`m sorry, I should have knocked, jeez I`m so sorry," Russ apologized profusely, shielding his eyes so he could stop staring at the sexy scene before him.

Brad tried to break the tension. "Um, can you give us a couple minutes, Russ?"

"What? Oh. Yes, of course."

Russ turned to walk out. Then he stopped and said, without turning around, "Oh, and, uh, it`s good to see you two back together again." He finally left and closed the door on his way out.

Brad and Kellie looked at each other. The tension broke and they laughed heartily. Reluctantly they let go of each other and got dressed.

As they kissed goodbye Brad gave Kellie`s butt a firm squeeze. "Do you think when we get home tonight we can pick up where we left off?"

Kellie grinned and traced her finger over Brad`s chest. "I think that can be arranged."

CPSIA information can be obtained
at www.ICGtesting.com
Printed in the USA
BVHW041050210121
598316BV00011B/850

The concentration etched on her face.
The strength uncoiling
from her body as she powered out of the hack. The graceful
follow-through as she extended her arm and let go of the rock.

"Don`t worry. I can handle things the rest of the
afternoon, there isn`t that much left to do. Now go on, Brad,
before you get cold feet!"
Brad shook his friend`s hand and patted him on the back.
"Thanks Russ," he said. Then he left the lounge/observation
area and hurried towards the ice.
She knew he watched her.
If it were anyone else, she was pretty sure she would be
entirely creeped out. Somehow, though, he was different.
Kellie and Brad both nodded. An uncomfortable silence hung
between them. Then Kellie said, "Well, I should really get going.
It was nice talking to you Brad."
With that, she headed for the change room, and Brad saw his
chance slipping away.
Even from a distance Brad could see the look of shock on her
face.

ISBN 978-1-80114-723-1
90000

9 781801 147231